THE NUMBER SYSTEM

BEVAN K. YOUSE
Emory University

DICKENSON PUBLISHING COMPANY
Belmont, California

To my parents

572.51
Y82m

PREFACE

The main purpose of this text is to present a careful development of the number system. By providing an axiomatic development of a mathematical system with which the student is already familiar, the text enhances his understanding of the axiomatic approach. This book is the outgrowth of two courses on the number system: one given for high school teachers of mathematics attending National Science Foundation Institutes, and the other given as a seminar course for undergraduate majors in mathematics. The material has proved successful in both courses, and it is hoped that the text will encourage an enthusiastic study of the number system by more students of mathematics.

Bevan K. Youse

CONTENTS

vii

1   THE NATURAL NUMBERS

1.1   Introduction

In the elementary use of numbers, the question "Is there a set of postulates, or axioms, from which all properties of numbers can be derived?" is not of great importance. It is only when we try to go more deeply into the nature of mathematics and mathematical reasoning that this and similar questions become important.

To better understand the *axiomatic approach* in developing the number system, let us recall our study of Euclidean plane geometry; this geometry deals with lines and points and with figures built up from lines and points. The lines and points of geometry are not objects in the physical world; they are, instead, abstractions from our intuitive ideas of straight lines and points. A straight line is an abstraction from a taut string or a ray of light. Geometry is an example of a *deductive science*; by this we mean that lines, points, and other geometric figures are proved to have certain properties by logical deductions from a certain set of basic assumptions called *postulates*, or *axioms*, of the geometry.

A *theorem* in geometry is a statement that some geometric figure has a certain property, and a *proof* of a theorem consists of logical deductions from basic assumptions to prove that the statement is true; of course, theorems already proved from the axioms can be used in the proof of any succeeding theorem. For the purpose of logical reasoning about lines and points, it is immaterial whether we know just what a straight line is or what a point is; the fundamental properties and relations between lines and points expressed in the basic assumptions are all we need to know. Geometric properties discovered by experiment and physical interpretations of point and line have no part in the logical deduction, except possibly to motivate the pattern of the deductive argument to prove a given theorem.

In the logical development of geometry, there are several problems to be solved concerning the set of postulates. (1) How do we choose, or find, the postulates from which we develop the geometry? (2) Is the set of postulates consistent? (3) Is there more than one set of postulates that could be used to develop the theory, and, if so, what criteria are used to decide which set of postulates to choose? To answer the first question as it pertains to Euclidean geometry: from those intuitive ideas about lines and points that seem valid, we abstract the simplest properties. These properties become the set of postulates. An example of such a property is that two distinct lines have at most one point in common.

When we ask whether or not the set of postulates is consistent, we are interested in knowing if the logical negation of one of the assumptions is a consequence of some of the other assumptions; in other words, is the set of postulates self-contradictory? Unfortunately, this is a question whose answer often depends on faith and not on any proof; for example, there is no proof that the set of postulates from Euclidean plane geometry is consistent. However, since in two thousand years no theorem and its negation have ever been deduced from the Euclidean postulates, it seems reasonably certain that this set of postulates is consistent.

More than one set of postulates could be used to develop a particular theory. If one has five consistent postulates from which five theorems can be proved, it would be logically correct to take the ten statements as basic assumptions, since they would be consistent and since any property that could be derived from the five assumptions in the first set could be derived from the ten assumptions in the second set. It is generally considered mathematically more elegant to use as few basic assumptions as possible to develop a theory; however, this basis for selection is sometimes ignored. Suppose, for example, that eight basic assumptions are necessary to develop a certain theory in an understandable manner for the high school student where, in fact, only four assumptions are logically necessary; it would then be reasonable to sacrifice some elegance for understanding if the use of only the four assumptions placed the theory out of the student's reach.

When we say that a statement in mathematics, such as the sum of the interior angles of a triangle is 180°, is a *true* statement, we mean that the statement is a logical consequence of the postulates. It is also true that the sum of the interior angles of a triangle is more than 180°; this is a logical consequence of the set of postulates for what is called elliptic plane geometry. It can be proved from the postulates of hyperbolic plane geometry that the sum of the interior angles of a triangle is less than 180°. It should be pointed out that if the set of Euclidean postulates is consistent, then it can be *proved* that the sets of postulates for elliptic and hyperbolic geometries are consistent; thus, although Euclidean geometry might be more useful in physical applications, Euclidean geometry is not logically superior to either of these geometries.

The idea that there should be a logical development of the number system, similar to that for geometry, did not occur to mathematicians until the nineteenth century, and it took many years for the theory to reach the form in which we present it. We begin by developing the natural numbers— 1, 2, 3, 4, 5, 6, etc.—from the postulational system first devised by the Italian mathematician and logician Giuseppe Peano (1858–1932).

1.2 Peano's Postulates

Before listing the postulates from which we derive all the properties of the set of natural numbers, let us call attention to undefined and primitive notions. We take "natural number" and "successor" as undefined concepts. Of course, natural number refers to "counting number"; 1 is the first counting number, and the successor of 1 is the "next" natural number, 2. If we denote the successor of the natural number n and n', then we define $1' = 2$, $2' = 3, 3' = 4, 4' = 5$, etc.

PEANO'S POSTULATES

1. 1 is a natural number.
2. For every natural number n, there exists one and only one natural number, denoted by n', called the *successor* of n.
3. If m and n are natural numbers and if $m' = n'$, then $m = n$. (No two different natural numbers have the same successor.)
4. For any natural number m, $m' \neq 1$. (No natural number has 1 as a successor.)
5. Let S be a collection of natural numbers with the following properties: (a) 1 is in S. (b) If the natural number k is in S, then k' is also in S. Then, the set S of natural numbers for which (a) and (b) are true contains all the natural numbers.

A mathematician often uses the words axiom and postulate interchangeably to mean any basic assumption. Many dictionaries state that the word axiom means "self-evident truth" while the word postulate means "assumed truth." We take Peano's postulates as assumptions and use them to prove such statements as the following.

1. For every pair of natural numbers m and n, we can uniquely assign to the pair a number called the sum, denoted by $m + n$, and a number called the product, denoted by $m \cdot n$, or mn.
2. For any natural numbers m, n, and p,

$$(m + n) + p = m + (n + p) \quad \text{and} \quad (mn)p = m(np).$$

3. For any pair of natural numbers m and n,

$$m + n = n + m \quad \text{and} \quad mn = nm.$$

4. For any natural numbers m, n, and p,

$$m(n + p) = (mn) + (mp).$$

5. For any pair of natural numbers m and n, one and only one of the following is true.
    (a) $m = n$.
    (b) There exists a natural number p such that $m + p = n$.
    (c) There exists a natural number q such that $m = n + q$.

1.3   Addition

In Theorem 1.1, we define the sum of any two natural numbers.

THEOREM 1.1   *Addition.*   For every pair m, n of natural numbers, one and only one natural number called the *sum*, denoted by $m + n$, is defined by the following:

(a) $m + 1 = m'$, for every natural number m.
(b) $m + n' = (m + n)'$, for every pair m, n.

Proof: We first prove that there is at least one natural number that can be assigned to $m + n$ for all m, n such that (a) and (b) are satisfied.

I.   For a particular natural number n, let S be the set of natural numbers m such that at least one natural number can be assigned to $m + n$ satisfying (a) and (b). (We show 1 is in S and then show k' is in S when k is in S; by postulate 5 we conclude S contains every natural number.)

Part 1.   *Let* $1 + n = n'$.

(A)   Letting $1 + n = n'$ implies $1 + 1 = 1'$ where $n = 1$. Furthermore, for $m + 1 = m'$ where $m = 1$, we have $1 + 1 = 1'$. Hence (a) is satisfied by the assignment $1 + n = n'$.

(B)   Letting $1 + n = n'$ implies $1 + n' = (n')'$. For $m + n' = (m + n)'$ where $m = 1$, we have $1 + n' = (1 + n)' = (n')'$. Hence, (b) is satisfied by letting $1 + n = n'$. Consequently, 1 is in S.

Part 2.   Assume k is in S; that is, assume at least one natural number can be assigned to $k + n$ satisfying (a) $k + 1 = k'$ and (b) $k + n' = (k + n)'$.

Let $k' + n = (k + n)'$; this assigns a natural number to $k' + n$ since we have assumed that at least one natural number is assigned to $k + n$ and since every natural number has a successor.

(A)   Letting $k' + n = (k + n)'$ implies $k' + 1 = (k + 1)'$ where $n = 1$; but, $(k + 1)' = (k')'$ so $k' + 1 = (k')'$.

For $m + 1 = m'$ where $m = k'$, we have $k' + 1 = (k')'$. Hence, (a) is satisfied by the assignment $k' + n = (k + n)'$.

(B) Letting $k' + n = (k + n)'$ implies $k' + n' = (k + n')'$; but, $k + n' = (k + n)'$ so $k' + n' = ((k + n)')'$. For $m + n' = (m + n)'$ where $m = k'$, we have $k' + n' = (k' + n)'$. By our assignment, $k' + n = (k + n)'$; hence, $k' + n' = ((k + n)')'$. Thus, (b) is satisfied.

By postulate 5, S contains all the natural numbers; therefore, there is at least one natural number that can be assigned to $m + n$ for all m and n which will satisfy (a) and (b).

II. We now use postulate 5 to prove that at most one natural number can be assigned to $m + n$ for all m and n which will satisfy (a) and (b).

Let m and n be natural numbers and let $m + n = r$ and $m + n = t$. Let S be the set of all natural numbers n such that $r = t$ for a given natural number m.

Part 1. For $n = 1$, $r = m + 1 = m'$ and $t = m + 1 = m'$. Since the successor of m is unique, $r = t$ and 1 is in S.

Part 2. Suppose k is in S. Thus, $m + k = r$ and $m + k = t$ implies $r = t$. If $m + k' = u$ and $m + k' = v$, $u = m + k' = (m + k)' = r'$ and $v = m + k' = (m + k)' = t'$. Since $r = t$, $r' = t'$ and $u = v$. Hence, k' is in S, and S contains every natural number.

Since Theorem 1.1 associates one and only one natural number with any given *pair* of natural numbers, it is said to define the *binary operation* called addition.† At present, the "string" $m + n + p$ is meaningless symbolism since it is not clear whether the sum $(m + n) + p$ or the sum $m + (n + p)$ is intended. In Theorem 1.2, we prove $(m + n) + p = m + (n + p)$; thereafter, parentheses are usually omitted since both sums are the same.

THEOREM 1.2 *Associative property of addition.* For natural numbers m, n, and p, $(m + n) + p = m + (n + p)$.

Proof: Let m and n be any given natural numbers. Let S be the set of all natural numbers p such that

$$(m + n) + p = m + (n + p).$$

(a) For $p = 1$,

$$(m + n) + 1 = (m + n)' \qquad \text{THEOREM 1.1}$$
$$= m + n' \qquad \text{THEOREM 1.1}$$
$$= m + (n + 1). \qquad \text{THEOREM 1.1}$$

† A binary operation on a set S is a relation with $S \times S$ as domain and S as range. See Section 1.8.

Thus, 1 is in S.

(b)   Assume k is in S.   Thus,

$$(m + n) + k = m + (n + k).$$

Now,

$$
\begin{aligned}
(m + n) + k' &= ((m + n) + k)' && \text{THEOREM 1.1} \\
&= (m + (n + k))' && \text{ASSUMPTION} \\
&= m + (n + k)' && \text{THEOREM 1.1} \\
&= m + (n + k'). && \text{THEOREM 1.1}
\end{aligned}
$$

Hence, k' is in S and S contains all natural numbers by postulate 5.   The theorem is proved.

In arithmetic, we learn that the sum obtained by adding a column of natural numbers "from top to bottom" is the same sum that is obtained by adding "from bottom to top."   To justify this fact, it is necessary to have not only the associative property of addition but also the property that $m + n = n + m$; this is called the *commutative property of addition.*

THEOREM 1.3   *Commutative property of addition.*   For every pair m, n of natural numbers, $m + n = n + m$.

Proof: Let m be any natural number and let S be the set of natural numbers n such that $m + n = n + m$.

(a)   For $n = 1$, $m + 1 = 1 + m$ for all m as a consequence of our assignment $1 + m = m'$ in the proof of Theorem 1.1.   Thus, 1 is in S.

(b)   Assume k is in S; that is, assume $m + k = k + m$.

$$
\begin{aligned}
m + k' &= (m + k)' && \text{THEOREM 1.1} \\
&= (k + m)' && \text{ASSUMPTION} \\
&= k + m' && \text{THEOREM 1.1} \\
&= k + (m + 1) && \text{THEOREM 1.1} \\
&= k + (1 + m) && \text{THEOREM 1.1} \\
&= (k + 1) + m && \text{THEOREM 1.2} \\
&= k' + m. && \text{THEOREM 1.1}
\end{aligned}
$$

Hence, k' is in S.   We conclude that $m + n = n + m$ for every pair of natural numbers m and n.

EXERCISES

1. Prove that $n' \neq n$ for every natural number n.
2. Prove that $m + n \neq n$ for every pair m, n of natural numbers.
3. Let S be the set containing 1 and the set of all natural numbers n for which there is a natural number m such that $m' = n$. Prove that S is the set of all natural numbers.
4. For every natural number m where $m \neq 1$, prove there exists exactly one natural number q such that $m = q'$. The natural number q is called the *predecessor* of m.
5. Prove that if m and n are natural numbers then $m + n \neq 1$.
6. If $m \neq n$, prove that $m + p \neq n + p$ where m, n, and p are natural numbers.

1.4 Multiplication

Theorems 1.4, 1.6, and 1.7 pertain to the binary operation of multiplication; the proofs are analogous to those given for the first three theorems.

THEOREM 1.4 *Multiplication*. For every pair m, n of natural numbers, one and only one natural number called the *product*, denoted by $m \cdot n$, or mn, is defined by the following:

(a) $m \cdot 1 = m$ for every natural number m.
(b) $m \cdot n' = (m \cdot n) + m$ for every pair m, n.

Proof: Left as an exercise for the reader.

The next theorem distinguishes between the two binary operations of addition and multiplication. We prove that multiplication "distributes" over addition; it is not true, as can be shown by a simple example, that addition distributes over multiplication. In other words, although $m(n + p) = (mn) + (mp)$ for all natural numbers m, n, and p,

$$m + (np) \neq (m + n)(m + p).$$

THEOREM 1.5 *Distributive property*. For natural numbers m, n, and p, $m(n + p) = (mn) + (mp)$.

Proof: Let m and n be natural numbers and let S be the set of all natural numbers p such that

$$m(n + p) = (mn) + (mp).$$

(a)   For $p = 1$,
$$m(n + 1) = mn' \qquad \text{THEOREM 1.1}$$
$$= (mn) + m \qquad \text{THEOREM 1.4}$$
$$= (mn) + (m \cdot 1) \qquad \text{THEOREM 1.4}$$

Thus, 1 is in S.

(b)   Assume $m(n + k) = (mn) + (mk)$; that is, assume k is in S. Then,
$$m(n + k') = m(n + k)' \qquad \text{THEOREM 1.1}$$
$$= (m(n + k)) + m \qquad \text{THEOREM 1.4}$$
$$= ((mn) + (mk)) + m \qquad \text{ASSUMPTION}$$
$$= (mn) + ((mk) + m) \qquad \text{THEOREM 1.2}$$
$$= (mn) + (mk'). \qquad \text{THEOREM 1.4}$$

Hence, k' is in S and S contains all natural numbers. Consequently $m(n + p) = (mn) + (mp)$ for all natural numbers m, n, and p.

THEOREM 1.6   *Commutative property of multiplication.*   For every pair m, n of natural numbers, $mn = nm$.

Proof: Left as an exercise for the reader.

THEOREM 1.7   *Associative property of multiplication.*   For natural numbers m, n, and p, $m(np) = (mn)p$.

Proof: Left as an exercise for the reader.

In order to avoid excessive use of parentheses, we agree that multiplication has precedence over addition; that is, $mn + n = (mn) + n$ and $mn + mp = (mn) + (mp)$.   This is a notational convenience; it has nothing to do with the relative importance of the two operations.

THEOREM 1.8   For every pair m, n of natural numbers, one and only one of the following is true.

(a) $m = n$

(b)   There exists a natural number p such that $m + p = n$.

(c)   There exists a natural number q such that $m = n + q$.

Proof: Part 1.   To prove that at most one of (a), (b), or (c) can be true, we first show that (a) and (b) cannot both be true.   By Exercise 2, page 7, $m + n \neq m$ for all m and n. If $m + p = n$, then $m \neq n$; otherwise, if $m = n$, then $m + p = m$, which is impossible. Similarly, both (a) and (c) cannot be true.

To show that (b) and (c) cannot both be true, let $m + p = n$ and $m = n + q$. Thus,

$$(n + q) + p = n$$

and $$n + (q + p) = n.$$ THEOREM 1.2

But $q + p$ is a natural number, and $n + (q + p) \neq n$ by Exercise 2, page 7. We conclude that (b) and (c) cannot both be true. Consequently, at most one of (a), (b), or (c) is true.

Part 2. We now prove, using postulate 5, that at least one of (a), (b), or (c) is true. For a natural number m, let S be the set of all n such that at least one of (a), (b), or (c) is true.

I. For $n = 1$, if $m = 1$, then $m = n$ and statement (a) is true. For $n = 1$, if $m \neq 1$, then there is exactly one natural number q such that $q' = m$ by Exercise 4, page 7. Since $q' = q + 1$, $m = q + 1$ and part (c) is true. Hence, 1 is in S.

II. Assume k is in S. Thus, exactly one of the following is true.

(1) $m = k$.
(2) $m + p = k$ for some p.
(3) $m = k + q$ for some q.

We now consider each case.

(1) If $m = k$, then $m' = k'$ and $m + 1 = k'$. Thus, (b) is true for $n = k'$.

(2) If $m + p = k$, then $(m + p)' = k'$ and $m + p' = k'$. Thus, (b) is true for $n = k'$.

(3) If $m = k + q$, we consider the cases where $q = 1$ and $q \neq 1$. If $q = 1$, $m = k + 1$ and $m = k'$. Thus, (a) is true for $n = k'$. If $q \neq 1$, there is one and only one natural number r such that $r' = q$; thus, $1 + r = q$. Consequently, $m = k + (1 + r)$ and $m = (k + 1) + r = k' + r$. Thus, (c) is true for $n = k'$.

We have proved k' is in S on the assumption that k was in S. By postulate 5, S contains every natural number and the theorem is proved.

EXERCISES

1. For every pair m, n of natural numbers, prove that $m'n' + 1 = (m' + n') + mn$.
2. If $1' = 2$, $2' = 3$, $3' = 4$, $4' = 5$, and $5' = 6$, prove that (a) $2 + 3 = 5$ and (b) $2 \cdot 3 = 6$.

3. If $1' = 2$, prove that $2n = n + n$ for every natural number n.
4. Show that addition does not "distribute" over multiplication.
5. Prove Theorem 1.4.
6. Prove Theorem 1.6.
7. Prove Theorem 1.7.
8. For all natural numbers m, n, and p, prove that $(m + n)p = mp + np$.

1.5   Equality

Up to this point, we have tacitly assumed certain properties of equality. Let us state these properties explicitly and consider two immediate consequences.

1. If m is a number, then $m = m$. This is called the *reflexive property* of equality.
2. If m and n are numbers and if $m = n$, then $n = m$. This is called the *symmetric property* of equality.
3. If m, n, and p are numbers and if $m = n$ and $n = p$, then $m = p$. This is called the *transitive property* of equality.

If m, n, and p are numbers and if $m = n$, then it follows that $m + p = n + p$ and $mp = np$ by the reflexive property of equality. It is often stated that equality is preserved if the same number is added to both sides of the equality or if both sides are multiplied by the same number.

If $m = p$ and $n = p$, then $p = n$ by the symmetric property and $m = n$ by the transitive property of equality. This fact can also be stated as "things equal to the same thing are equal to each other."

1.6   Order

For every pair m, n of natural numbers, m is said to be *less than n*, denoted by $m < n$, if and only if there exists a natural number q such that $m + q = n$. We call $m < n$ an *inequality*.

THEOREM 1.9   *Trichotomy property.* For any pair m, n of natural numbers, one and only one of the following is true: (a) $m = n$, (b) $m < n$, (c) $n < m$.

Proof: A direct consequence of Theorem 1.8 and the definition of $<$.

For every pair m, n of natural numbers, m is said to be *greater than n*, denoted by $m > n$, if and only if $n < m$. Furthermore, $m \leq n$ if and only if $m < n$ or $m = n$; similarly, $m \geq n$ if and only if $m > n$ or $m = n$.

THEOREM 1.10 *Transitive property of inequality.* If m, n, and p are natural numbers such that $m < n$ and $n < p$, then $m < p$.

Proof: If $m < n$, there exists a natural number s such that

(1) $m + s = n$.

If $n < p$, there exists a natural number t such that

(2) $n + t = p$.

Substituting (1) in (2), $(m + s) + t = p$. Hence,

$$m + (s + t) = p.$$

Since $s + t$ is a natural number, $m < p$ by definition of less than.

Any set of numbers for which $<$ (less than) is defined and that has both the trichotomy property and transitive property is called an *ordered set.* Two important properties of the ordered set of natural numbers are given in the following theorem.

THEOREM 1.11 If m, n, and p are natural numbers and if $m < n$, then each of the following is true:

(a) $m + p < n + p$ and   (b) $mp < np$.

Proof: (a) If $m < n$, there exists a natural number s such that

$$m + s = n.$$

Hence, $(m + s) + p = n + p.$

Since

$$(m + s) + p = m + (s + p) = m + (p + s) = (m + p) + s,$$

$$(m + p) + s = n + p.$$

Consequently, $m + p < n + p.$

(b) If $m < n$, there exists a natural number s such that

$$m + s = n.$$

Thus, $(m + s)p = np$

and $mp + sp = np.$

Since sp is a natural number, $mp < np$.

We now prove for the set of natural numbers what are called the cancellation properties of addition and multiplication for equalities and inequalities.

THEOREM 1.12 *Cancellation property of addition.* Let m, n, and p be natural numbers. If $m + p < n + p$, $m + p = n + p$, or $m + p > n + p$, then $m < n$, $m = n$, or $m > n$, respectively.

Proof: Assume $m + p < n + p$. We conclude that $m \neq n$, for if $m = n$, then $m + p = n + p$, a contradiction to our assumption. Similarly, if $m > n$, then $m + p > n + p$, which also contradicts the assumption that $m + p < n + p$. Hence, by the trichotomy property we conclude that if $m + p < n + p$, then $m < n$.

Similarly, $m + p = n + p$ implies $m = n$, and $m + p > n + p$ implies $m > n$.

THEOREM 1.13 *Cancellation property of multiplication.* Let m, n, and p be natural numbers. If $mp = np$, $mp < np$, or $mp > np$, then $m = n$, $m < n$, or $m > n$, respectively.

Proof: Left as an exercise for the reader.

EXERCISES

1. Prove that $n \geq 1$ for every natural number n.
2. For natural numbers m, n, p, and q, if $m < n$ and $p < q$, then $mp < nq$.
3. For natural numbers m, n, p, and q, if $m < n$ and $p < q$, then $m + p < n + q$.
4. For every natural number n, no natural number m exists such that $n < m$ and $m < n + 1$.
5. For natural numbers m, n, and p, if $m = pn$ and $p \neq 1$, then $n < m$.
6. For natural numbers m, n, and p, if $m \leq n$ and $n < p$, then $m < p$.
7. For natural numbers m and n, if $m > n$, then $m \geq n + 1$.
8. For natural numbers m and n, if $m < n + 1$, then $m \leq n$.
9. For natural numbers m, n, p, and q, if $m \leq n$ and $p < q$, then $m + p < n + q$ and $mp < nq$.
10. Prove Theorem 1.13.

1.7 Well-Ordering Property

Let S be a set of natural numbers. If there is a natural number t in S such that $t \leq n$ for every n in S, then t is called the *least element* in S. We now prove that every non-empty set of natural numbers has a least element in the set; this is called the *well-ordering property* of the set of natural numbers.

THEOREM 1.14 *Well-ordering property.* Every non-empty set S of natural numbers has a least element in S.

Proof: Let T be the set of all natural numbers t such that $t \le y$ for every y in S. By Exercise 1, page 12, $1 \le n$ for every natural number n; hence, 1 is in T. Furthermore, if y is in S then $y + 1$ is not in T since $y + 1 > y$.

Now, there is a natural number p in T such that $p + 1$ is not in T; this is true since if 1 is in T, and if $p + 1$ is in T whenever p is in T, then by postulate 5 T is the set of all natural numbers which contradicts the fact there exists at least one natural number not in T.

If p is in T, then $p \le y$ for all y in S by definition of T. If p is not in S, then $p < y$ for every y in S. By Exercise 7, page 12, $p + 1 \le y$ if $p < y$; hence, $p + 1$ is in T, a contradiction. Consequently, p is in S. Since $p \le y$ for all y in S and since p is in S, the natural number p is the least natural number in S.

1.8 Relations

Let S be a set. If x and y are elements of S, then (x, y) is called an *ordered pair* of elements of S. For the ordered pair (x, y), x is called the *first element*, or *first coordinate*, and y is called the *second element*, or *second coordinate*. Two ordered pairs (x, y) and (u, v) are *equal* if and only if $x = u$ and $y = v$. The set of ordered pairs with all the elements of S as first and second elements is called the *cartesian product of S with itself*; it is denoted by $S \times S$. For example, if $S = \{1, 2, 3\}$, then

$$S \times S = \{(1, 1), (1, 2), (1, 3), (2, 1), (2, 2), (2, 3), (3, 1), (3, 2), (3, 3)\}$$

is the cartesian product of S with itself.

A *relation R on S is any subset of $S \times S$*. For example, $R = \{(1, 2), (1, 3), (2, 3)\}$ is a relation on S where $S = \{1, 2, 3\}$. The *domain* of a relation is the set of all first elements and the *range* of a relation is the set of all second elements. The domain of the given relation R is $\{1, 2\}$ and the range is $\{2, 3\}$.

Let R be a relation on S. An element x in S is said to be in R relation to y if and only if (x, y) is an element in R. Furthermore, for a relation R on a set S, we write xRy if and only if (x, y) is in R. If $<$ is used to denote the set R in our example, then $< = \{(1, 2), (1, 3), (2, 3)\}$ and $1 < 2$ since $(1, 2)$ is in the set $<$. The set $<$ is the less than relation on S. In general, if N is the set of natural numbers, then

$$\{(m, m + p) \quad \text{where } m \text{ and } p \text{ are natural numbers}\}$$

is the less than relation on N. Furthermore,

$$\{(m, m) \quad \text{where } m \text{ is a natural number}\}$$

is the equals relation on N.

There is an important class of relations on any set S called *equivalence relations*. Let S be a set and let R be a relation on S; that is, R is a subset of $S \times S$. The relation R is called an equivalence relation, provided each of the following is true.

1. For *every* x in S, (x, x) is in R. This is called the *reflexive property*.
2. If (x, y) is in R, then (y, x) is in R. This is called the *symmetric property*.
3. If (x, y) and (y, z) are in R, then (x, z) is in R. This is called the *transitive property*.

It is obvious that the equals relation on N is an equivalence relation. The less-than relation has the transitive property; however, the less-than relation is not an equivalence relation since it has neither the symmetric nor the reflexive properties.

We now consider two relations whose *domains and ranges are sets of ordered pairs of natural numbers*. In other words, the first and second elements of the relations are themselves ordered pairs of natural numbers.

EXAMPLES

1. Let N be the set of natural numbers and let $S = N \times N$. If (x, y) and (u, v) are elements of S, we define a relation $\sim$ to be the subset of $S \times S$ such that

$$\sim = \{((x, y), (u, v)) \quad \text{such that} \quad x + v = y + u\}.$$

Thus, $((2, 3), (7, 8))$ is an element of $\sim$, $(2, 3)$ is the first element and $(7, 8)$ is the second element, and $(2, 3) \sim (7, 8)$. In general, $(x, y) \sim (u, v)$ if and only if $x + v = y + u$. We prove that $\sim$ is an equivalence relation on S.

   (a) For (x, y) in S, $(x, y) \sim (x, y)$ since $x + y = y + x$. In other words, $((x, y), (x, y))$ is in $\sim$ and the relation has the reflexive property.
   (b) If $(x, y) \sim (u, v)$, then $x + v = y + u$ by definition of the relation. By the commutative property of addition for the natural numbers, $v + x = u + y$; and by the symmetric property of equality, $u + y = v + x$. Thus, $(u, v) \sim (x, y)$ and the relation has the symmetric property.

(c) If $(x, y) \sim (u, v)$ and $(u, v) \sim (w, z)$, then

$$x + v = y + u$$

and

$$u + z = v + w.$$

Adding, $$x + v + u + z = u + v + w + y$$

and

$$x + z = y + w$$

by the cancellation property of addition for the natural numbers. Hence, $(x, y) \sim (w, z)$ and $\sim$ has the transitive property.

2. Let N be the set of natural numbers and let $S = N \times N$. If (x, y) and (u, v) are elements of S, we define a relation $\simeq$ to be the subset of $S \times S$ defined by

$$\simeq = \{((x, y), (u, v)) \quad \text{such} \quad \text{that} \quad xv = yu\}.$$

We leave as an exercise for the reader to prove that $\simeq$ is an equivalence relation.

Let R be an equivalence relation on a set S and let s be any element of S. The set of all x in S such that (s, x) is in R is called an *equivalence set*, or *equivalence class*; it is denoted by s^R. In other words, s^R is the set of all x such that sRx for some s in S. For the equals relation on N, each equivalence set contains exactly one element; that is, for the natural number m, the equivalence set $m^=$ is $\{m\}$. For the equivalence relation $\sim$ in Example 1, the equivalence sets contain infinitely many elements; that is, for each element (a, b) in S,

$$(a, b)^\sim = \{(x, y) \quad \text{such that} \quad a + y = b + x\}.$$

Thus, $(2, 3)^\sim$ contains such elements as $(2, 3)$, $(7, 8)$, $(13, 14)$, etc. It should be noted that since $(2, 3) \sim (7, 8)$, the equivalence sets $(2, 3)^\sim$ and $(7, 8)^\sim$ are equal; a proof of this fact follows.

If $(a, b) \sim (c, d)$, we want to prove that $(a, b)^\sim = (c, d)^\sim$. Since $(a, b)^\sim = (c, d)^\sim$ is set equality, we need to show that each set contains exactly the same elements. If $(a, b) \sim (c, d)$, then $(c, d) \sim (a, b)$ by the symmetric property of the equivalence relation. If (x, y) is any element in $(a, b)^\sim$, then $(a, b) \sim (x, y)$; since $(c, d) \sim (a, b)$ and $(a, b) \sim (x, y)$, we conclude that $(c, d) \sim (x, y)$ by the transitive property of the equivalence relation. Thus, (x, y) is an element in $(c, d)^\sim$. Consequently, any element in $(a, b)^\sim$ is an element in $(c, d)^\sim$, and $(a, b)^\sim$ is a subset of $(c, d)^\sim$; symbolically, $(a, b)^\sim \subseteq (c, d)^\sim$. Similarly, we can prove that every element in $(c, d)^\sim$ is in $(a, b)^\sim$; that is, $(c, d)^\sim \subseteq (a, b)^\sim$. Thus, $(a, b)^\sim = (c, d)^\sim$ by the definition of set equality.

If (a, b) and (c, d) are any two elements in S, then the equivalence sets $(a, b)^\sim$ and $(c, d)^\sim$ are either equal or have no elements in common. If the two equivalence sets $(a, b)^\sim$ and $(c, d)^\sim$ have at least one element (x, y) in common, then $(a, b) \sim (x, y)$ and $(c, d) \sim (x, y)$. Thus, $(x, y) \sim (c, d)$ by the symmetric property and $(a, b) \sim (c, d)$ by the transitive property. As a consequence of what was proved in the preceding paragraph, $(a, b)^\sim = (c, d)^\sim$. Sets having no elements in common are called *disjoint sets*; thus, equivalence sets are either equal or disjoint.

We say that an equivalence relation R on a set S *induces a partition on S*; this means that S can be expressed as the union of the disjoint equivalence sets of S. For the equivalence relation $\sim$ on S, S is the union of the infinitely many disjoint equivalence sets $(1, 1)^\sim, (1, 2)^\sim, \cdots, (1, n)^\sim, \cdots$ and $(2, 1)^\sim, (3, 1)^\sim, \cdots, (n, 1)^\sim, \cdots$.

EXERCISES

1. Let N be the set of natural numbers and let $S = N \times N$. Let (x, y) and (u, v) be elements of S and define a relation $\simeq$ by

$$\simeq = \{((x, y), (u, v)) \text{ such that } xv = yu\}.$$

   (a) Prove that $\simeq$ is an equivalence relation.
   (b) List six elements of the equivalence set $(2, 3)^\simeq$.

2. Let N be the set of natural numbers and let $S = N \times N$. Let (x, y) and (u, v) be elements of S and define a relation λ by

$$\lambda = \{((x, y), (u, v)) \text{ such that } xv(y + u) = yu(x + v)\}.$$

   (a) Prove that λ is an equivalence relation on S.
   (b) List ten elements of the equivalence set $(1, 1)^\lambda$.
   (c) List all of the elements of the equivalence set $(1, 2)^\lambda$.
   (d) List at least two elements of the equivalence set $(8, 3)^\lambda$.
   (e) List all elements of the equivalence set $(8, 3)^\lambda$.

3. Let S be any non-empty set and let R be an equivalence relation defined on S. If v and w are elements of S, prove that the equivalence sets v^R and w^R are equal if and only if vRw.

4. Let N be the set of natural numbers and let $S = N \times N$. Let (x, y) and (u, v) be elements of S and define a relation γ by

$$\gamma = \{((x, y), (u, v)) \text{ such that } xu(y + v) = yv(x + u)\}.$$

   (a) Does this relation have the reflexive property? Justify.
   (b) Does this relation have the symmetric property? Justify.
   (c) Does this relation have the transitive property? Justify.

5. Let $\beta = \{(x, y) \text{ where } x \text{ and } y \text{ are natural numbers and } x \leq y\}$.
   (a) Does this relation on the set of natural numbers have the reflexive property? (b) Symmetric property? (c) Transitive property?

2

THE INTEGERS

2.1 Addition

In Chapter 1, we proved that if S is the cartesian product of the set N of natural numbers with itself, then

$$\{((x, y), (u, v)) \quad \text{such that} \quad x + v = y + u\}$$

is an equivalence relation $\sim$ on S; furthermore, the equivalence sets are disjoint and $(a, b)^\sim = (c, d)^\sim$ if and only if $a + d = b + c$. We call the equivalence set $(a, b)^\sim$ an *integer* and the set of all such equivalence sets the set of integers. We *define addition* for the set of integers and prove various properties the set has with respect to this operation.

Let $(a, b)^\sim$ and $(c, d)^\sim$ be two integers. The integer $(a + c, b + d)^\sim$ is called the *sum* of the two given integers; symbolically,

$$(a, b)^\sim + (c, d)^\sim = (a + c, b + d)^\sim.†$$

We first prove that the set of integers has the commutative and associative properties of addition.

THEOREM 2.1 *Commutative property of addition.* If $(a, b)^\sim$ and $(c, d)^\sim$ are integers, then

$$(a, b)^\sim + (c, d)^\sim = (c, d)^\sim + (a, b)^\sim.$$

† It would be more appropriate to write

$$(a, b)^\sim \oplus (c, d)^\sim = (a + c, b + d)^\sim$$

to distinguish between addition for integers and addition for natural numbers. But, since there should be little opportunity for confusion by not making this distinction, we do not complicate our notation unnecessarily.

Proof: By definition,

$$(a, b)^\sim + (c, d)^\sim = (a + c, b + d)^\sim$$

and

$$(c, d)^\sim + (a, b)^\sim = (c + a, d + b)^\sim.$$

Since $a + c = c + a$ and $b + d = d + b$ by the commutative property of addition for the natural numbers, we conclude that

$$(a + c, b + d)^\sim = (c + a, d + b)^\sim \ ;$$

thus, $$(a, b)^\sim + (c, d)^\sim = (c, d)^\sim + (a, b)^\sim.$$

THEOREM 2.2 *Associative property of addition.* For integers $(a, b)^\sim, (c, d)^\sim,$ and $(e, f)^\sim,$

$$[(a, b)^\sim + (c, d)^\sim] + (e, f)^\sim = (a, b)^\sim + [(c, d)^\sim + (e, f)^\sim].$$

Proof: Left as an exercise for the reader.

The integer $(a, a)^\sim$ has an important property with respect to addition; the sum of it and any given integer is the given integer.

THEOREM 2.3   If $(c, d)^\sim$ is any integer, then

$$(c, d)^\sim + (a, a)^\sim = (c, d)^\sim.$$

Proof: $(c, d)^\sim + (a, a)^\sim = (c + a, d + a)^\sim$ by definition of addition for the integers. Since $(x, y)^\sim = (u, v)^\sim$ if and only if $x + v = y + u$, we conclude $(c + a, d + a)^\sim = (c, d)^\sim$ by using the definition of equality and the commutative and associative properties of addition for the natural numbers; thus, the theorem is proved.

A number having the property expressed in Theorem 2.3 is called an *additive identity.* The proof that there is only one additive identity for the set of integers is left as an exercise for the reader; henceforth, $(a, a)^\sim$ is, referred to as *the* additive identity for the set of integers.

THEOREM 2.4 *Cancellation property of addition.* If $(a, b)^\sim,$ $(c, d)^\sim,$ and $(e, f)^\sim$ are integers, and if $(a, b)^\sim + (e, f)^\sim = (c, d)^\sim + (e, f)^\sim$ then $(a, b)^\sim = (c, d)^\sim.$

Proof: From $(a, b)^\sim + (e, f)^\sim = (c, d)^\sim + (e, f)^\sim,$ we conclude that $(a + e, b + f)^\sim = (c + e, d + f)^\sim.$ Thus, $a + e + d + f = b + f + c + e$ which implies $a + d = b + c.$ Hence, $(a, b)^\sim = (c, d)^\sim.$

2.2   Multiplication

If $(a, b)^\sim$ and $(c, d)^\sim$ are two integers, then we define the integer $(ac + bd, ad + bc)^\sim$ to be the *product* of the given integers; symbolically,

$$(a, b)^\sim(c, d)^\sim = (ac + bd, ad + bc)^\sim.$$

We first prove that the set of integers has the commutative and associative properties of multiplication.

THEOREM 2.5   *Commutative property of multiplication.*   If $(a, b)^\sim$ and $(c, d)^\sim$ are integers, then

$$(a, b)^\sim \cdot (c, d)^\sim = (c, d)^\sim \cdot (a, b)^\sim.$$

Proof: By definition of multiplication,

$$(a, b)^\sim \cdot (c, d)^\sim = (ac + bd, ad + bc)^\sim$$

and $(c, d)^\sim \cdot (a, b)^\sim = (ca + db, cb + da)^\sim.$

Since $ac + bd = ca + db$ and $ad + bc = cb + da$ by the commutative properties of addition and multiplication for natural numbers,

$$(ac + bd, ad + bc)^\sim = (ca + db, cb + da)^\sim$$

and the theorem is proved.

THEOREM 2.6   *Associative property of multiplication.*   If $(a, b)^\sim$, $(c, d)^\sim$, and $(e, f)^\sim$ are integers, then

$$[(a, b)^\sim \cdot (c, d)^\sim] \cdot (e, f)^\sim = (a, b)^\sim \cdot [(c, d)^\sim \cdot (e, f)^\sim].$$

Proof: Left as an exercise for the reader.

We proved in Theorem 2.3 that the additive identity $(a, a)^\sim$ has the property that the sum of it and any integer is the given integer; we prove now that the product of $(a, a)^\sim$ and any integer is $(a, a)^\sim$.

THEOREM 2.7   If $(c, d)^\sim$ is any integer, then

$$(a, a)^\sim \cdot (c, d)^\sim = (a, a)^\sim.$$

Proof: By definition of multiplication,

$$(a, a)^\sim \cdot (c, d)^\sim = (ac + ad, ad + ac)^\sim.$$

Since $ac + ad = ad + ac$, we conclude that

$$(ac + ad, ad + ac)^\sim = (a, a)^\sim;$$

the theorem is proved.

The integer $(a + 1, a)^\sim$ has the important property that its product with any given integer is the given integer; this is proved in the subsequent theorem.

THEOREM 2.8   If $(c, d)^\sim$ is any integer, then

$$(a + 1, a)^\sim \cdot (c, d)^\sim = (c, d)^\sim.$$

Proof:
$$
\begin{aligned}
(a + 1, a)^\sim \cdot (c, d)^\sim &= (ac + c + ad, ad + d + ac)^\sim \\
&= (ac + ad + c, ac + ad + d)^\sim \\
&= (c, d)^\sim.
\end{aligned}
$$

A number having the property expressed in Theorem 2.8 is called a *multiplicative identity*. The proof that there is only one multiplicative identity for the set of integers is left as an exercise for the reader; henceforth, $(a + 1, a)^\sim$ is referred to as *the* multiplicative identity for the set of integers.

THEOREM 2.9   *Distributive property.*   For integers $(a, b)^\sim$, $(c, d)^\sim$, and $(e, f)^\sim$,

$$(a, b)^\sim \cdot [(c, d)^\sim + (e, f)^\sim] = (a, b)^\sim \cdot (c, d)^\sim + (a, b)^\sim \cdot (e, f)^\sim.$$

Proof:
(1) $(a, b)^\sim [(c, d)^\sim + (e, f)^\sim]$
$$
\begin{aligned}
&= (a, b)^\sim \cdot (c + e, d + f)^\sim \\
&= (ac + ae + bd + bf, ad + af + bc + be)^\sim
\end{aligned}
$$
(2) $(a, b)^\sim \cdot (c, d)^\sim + (a, b)^\sim \cdot (e, f)^\sim$
$$
\begin{aligned}
&= (ac + bd, ad + bc)^\sim + (ae + bf, af + be)^\sim \\
&= (ac + bd + ae + bf, ad + bc + af + be)^\sim.
\end{aligned}
$$

Comparing the results in (1) and (2), we conclude that the theorem is true.

For the integer $(a, b)^\sim$, since a and b are natural numbers one and only one of the following is true: (1) $a = b$, (2) $a < b$, or (3) $a > b$. We simplify our notation for integers in the following way.

1.   The symbol 0 denotes the integer $(a, b)^\sim$ if $a = b$. This integer, which is the additive identity, is called *zero*.
2.   The symbol $+p$ is used to denote the integer $(a, b)^\sim$ if $a > b$ and p is the natural number such that $a = b + p$; such integers are called *positive integers*.

3. The symbol $-q$ is used to denote the integer $(a, b)^\sim$ if $a < b$ and q is the natural number such that $a + q = b$; such integers are called *negative integers*.

Thus, $(6, 6)^\sim = 0, (8, 3)^\sim = +5, (7, 8)^\sim = -1, (8, 7)^\sim = +1, (4, 12)^\sim = -8$, etc.

For any integer x, we have already proved that $x + 0 = x, (x)(+1) = x$, and $(x)(0) = 0$. Since $+3 = (4, 1)^\sim$ and $-3 = (1, 4)^\sim$,

$$(+3) + (-3) = (4, 1)^\sim + (1, 4)^\sim$$
$$= (5, 5)^\sim$$
$$= 0.$$

In general, if x is any integer, then there exists one and only one integer y called the *additive inverse of* x such that $x + y = 0$. To show that an additive inverse of $x = (a, b)^\sim$ exists, let $y = (b, a)^\sim$ and it follows that $x + y = 0$. Furthermore, the additive inverse of a positive integer is a negative integer, the additive inverse of a negative integer is a positive integer, and the additive inverse of zero is zero.

To prove that the additive inverse of a given integer is unique, assume there are two integers y and z such that $x + y = 0$ and $x + z = 0$. Hence,

$$x + y = x + z.$$

By the cancellation property of addition for integers,

$$y = z.$$

The proof that the product, or sum, of two positive integers is a positive integer is left as an exercise for the reader; this can be done by proving that for positive integers (a, b) and (c, d) where $a > b$ and $c > d$ it follows that $a + c > b + d$ and $ac + bd > ad + bc$. Furthermore, the sum of two negative integers is a negative integer, but the product of two negative integers is a positive integer. The fact that the product of two positive integers is positive and the product of two negative integers is positive serves as a distinguishing property between the set of positive and the set of negative integers. In other words, the sum and product of any two numbers in one set is always in the set while for the other set this is not true.

EXERCISES

1. Prove that the product of two positive integers is a positive integer.
2. Prove that the sum of two positive integers is a positive integer.
3. Prove that the sum of two negative integers is a negative integer.
4. Prove the product of two negative integers is a positive integer.

5. Prove that the product of a positive integer and a negative integer is a negative integer.
6. Given that the sum of two natural numbers a and b is the natural number c, prove that $(+a) + (+b) = +c$. Hint: $+a = (a + 1, 1)^\sim$.
7. Given that the product of two natural numbers a and b is c, prove that $(+a)(+b) = +c$. See Exercise 6.
8. Prove Theorem 2.2.
9. Prove Theorem 2.6.
10. Prove that the set of integers has only one additive identity.
11. Prove the cancellation property of addition for equality using the associative property of addition and the fact that each integer has an additive inverse. Hint: If $x + z = y + z$, then $(x + z) + t = (y + z) + t$ where t is the additive inverse of z.
12. Prove that there is only one multiplicative identity in the set of integers.

2.3   Order

The less-than relation is defined for integers in the following way: $x < y$ if and only if there is a positive integer z such that $x + z = y$. Furthermore, $y > x$ if and only if $x < y$; $x \leq y$ if and only if $x < y$ or $x = y$; and $x \geq y$ if and only if $x > y$ or $x = y$.

THEOREM 2.10   An integer x is positive if and only if $x > 0$.

Proof: Part 1.   Assume x is a positive integer.   Since $0 + x = x$ and since x is positive, $0 < x$ as a consequence of the definition of the less than relation.   Hence, $x > 0$.

Part 2.   Assume $x > 0$.   By definition of the less-than relation, $0 < x$ implies that there is a positive integer y such that $0 + y = x$.   Since $0 + y = y$, we conclude that $x = y$ and x is positive.

THEOREM 2.11   An integer x is negative if and only if $x < 0$.

Proof: Left as an exercise for the reader.

THEOREM 2.12   *Trichotomy property.*   If x and y are integers, then one and only one of the following is true:

(1) $x = y$,   (2) $x < y$,   or   (3) $x > y$.

Proof: Let $x = (a, b)\tilde{}$ and $y = (c, d)\tilde{}$ where a, b, c, and d are natural numbers.

(1) $(a, b)\tilde{} = (c, d)\tilde{}$ if and only if $a + d = b + c$.
(2) $(a, b)\tilde{} < (c, d)\tilde{}$ if and only if $(a, b)\tilde{} + (u + s, u)\tilde{} = (c, d)\tilde{}$ where u and s are natural numbers. But

$$(a, b)\tilde{} + (u + s, u)\tilde{} = (c, d)\tilde{}$$

if and only if

$$(a + u + s, b + u)\tilde{} = (c, d)\tilde{}$$

if and only if

$$a + u + s + d = b + u + c$$

if and only if

$$a + d < b + c.$$

(3) Similarly, we can prove that $(a, b)\tilde{} > (c, d)\tilde{}$ if and only if $a + d > b + c$.

Since one and only one of $a + d = b + c$, $a + d < b + c$, $a + d > b + c$ is true, we conclude the theorem is true.

THEOREM 2.13 *Transitive property of inequality.* Let x, y, and z be integers. If $x < y$ and $y < z$, then $x < z$.

Proof: If $x < y$, then there is a positive integer s such that

(1) $$x + s = y.$$

If $y < z$, then there is a positive integer t such that

(2) $$y + t = z.$$

Substituting (1) in (2),

$$(x + s) + t = z$$

and $x + (s + t) = z$ by the associative property of addition. Since s and t are positive integers, their sum is a positive integer; hence, $x < z$ as a consequence of the definition of the less than relation.

Since the set of integers has the trichotomy and transitive properties with respect to the less than relation, the set of integers is an ordered set.

As we have seen, many of the properties of the set of integers are analogous to the properties of the set of natural numbers; however, there are some significant differences. Although we can prove the cancellation property of addition for the integers, we must assume $z \neq 0$ to prove that $xz = yz$ implies $x = y$. We can prove that if x, y, and z are integers $x < y$ if and only if $x + z < y + z$; however, it is not necessarily true that $x < y$ if and only if $xz < yz$.

THEOREM 2.14   Let x, y, and z be integers. $x < y$ if and only if $x + z < y + z$.

Proof: Part 1.   If $x < y$, then there is a positive integer t such that $x + t = y$.   Thus,

$$(x + t) + z = y + z,$$

and by the associative and commutative properties of addition for the integers we conclude that

$$(x + z) + t = y + z.$$

Since t is a positive integer, $x + z < y + z$ by definition of the less than relation.

Part 2.   If $x + y < y + z$, then there is a positive integer t such that $(x + z) + t = y + z$.   By the associative and commutative properties of addition,

$$(x + t) + z = y + z.$$

By the cancellation property of addition for the integers,

$$x + t = y.$$

Since t is a positive integer, $x < y$.

THEOREM 2.15   Let x, y, and z be integers.   If $x < y$ and $x > 0$, then $xz < yz$.

Proof: If $x < y$, then there is a positive integer t such that $x + t = y$. Thus, $(x + t)z = yz$ and

$$xz + tz = yz.$$

Since t and z are positive integers, the product tz is a positive integer and we conclude that $xz < yz$.

THEOREM 2.16   Let x, y, and z be integers.   If $x < y$ and $x < 0$, then $xz > yz$.

Proof: If $x < y$, then there is a positive integer t such that $x + t = y$. Thus, $xz + tz = yz$. Since t is positive and z is negative, the product tz is a negative integer. Thus, $tz < 0$; adding $(-tz)$ to both sides of the inequality, we conclude that $0 < (-tz)$. Adding $(-tz)$ to both sides of the equality $xz + tz = yz$, we get

$$xz = yz + (-tz).$$

Since $(-tz)$ is positive, $yz < xz$, or $xz > yz$, and the theorem is proved.

THEOREM 2.17   For integers x, y, and z, if $z \neq 0$, then $xz = yz$ implies $x = y$.

Proof: If $z \neq 0$, then $z > 0$ or $z < 0$. We show that assuming $x \neq y$ leads to a contradiction. If $x \neq y$, then $x > y$ or $x < y$.

If $x > 0$ and $x > y$, then $xz > yz$; if $z > 0$ and $x < y$, then $xz < yz$. In either case, $xz \neq yz$, which is contrary to the hypothesis.

If $z < 0$ and $x > y$, then $xz < yz$; if $z < 0$ and $x < y$, then $xz > yz$. In either case, $xz \neq yz$, which is contrary to hypothesis. Since assuming that $x \neq y$ leads to a contradiction, we conclude $x = y$.

If the natural number a is paired with the positive integer $+a$, then this gives a one-to-one correspondence between the set of natural numbers and the set of positive integers. By this correspondence, the sum $a + b$ is paired with the sum $(+a) + (+b)$ and the product ab is paired with the product $(+a)(+b)$. See Exercises 6 and 7, page 22. In order to describe this situation, we say that the set of natural numbers is *isomorphic* to the set of positive integers. Roughly speaking, the sets are indistinguishable since "natural numbers" and "positive integers" are essentially two different names for the same set of numbers.

EXERCISES

1. Prove Theorem 2.11.
2. Let x, y, and z be integers. Prove that if $xz < yz$ and $z > 0$, then $x < y$.
3. Let x, y, and z be integers. Prove that if $xz < yz$ and $z < 0$, then $x > y$.
4. (a) Let I be the set of integers and let $S = I \times I$. Let (x, y) and (u, v) be elements of S where $y \neq 0$ and $v \neq 0$. Prove that

$$* = \{((x, y), (u, v)) \text{ such that } xv = yu\}$$

is an equivalence relation.
    (b) List six elements in each of the following equivalence sets: $(2, 3)^*$, $(6, 1)^*$, $(2, 3)^*$, $(-5, -10)^*$, $(-3, 4)^*$, and $(0, 9)^*$.

3   THE RATIONAL NUMBERS

3.1 Ordered Field Properties

A set of elements F with two binary operations $+$ and $\cdot$ defined is called a *field* if F has the following properties.

1. *Addition.* An element in F, denoted by $x + y$, called the *sum*, is uniquely determined for every pair x, y in F.
2. *Commutative property of addition.* $x + y = y + x$ for every pair x, y in F.
3. *Associative property of addition.* $x + (y + z) = (x + y) + z$ for every x, y, and z in F.
4. *Additive identity.* There exists an element in F denoted by 0 called an additive identity such that $x + 0 = x$ for every x in F.
5. *Additive inverses.* For every element x in F, there exists an element in F called an additive inverse of x and denoted by $-x$ such that $x + (-x) = 0$.
6. *Multiplication.* An element in F, denoted by $x \cdot y$, or xy, called the *product*, is uniquely determined for every x, y in F.
7. *Commutative property of multiplication.* $xy = yz$ for every pair x, y in F.
8. *Associative property of multiplication.* $x(yz) = (xy)z$ for every x, y, and z in F.
9. *Multiplicative identity.* There exists an element in F distinct from 0, called a multiplicative identity and denoted by 1, such that $x \cdot 1 = x$ for every x in F.
10. *Multiplicative inverses.* For every element $x \neq 0$ in F, there exists an element in F, called a multiplicative inverse of x and denoted by x^{-1}, such that $x \cdot x^{-1} = 1$.

11.   *Distributive property.* $x(y + z) = xy + xz$ for every x, y, and
z in F.

As discussed earlier, a set F is called an ordered set if a less than
relation defined on F has the transitive and trichotomy properties. If F
is an ordered set with the field properties, if $x < y$ implies $x + z = y + z$,
and if $x < y$ and $z > 0$ implies $xz < yz$, then F is called an *ordered field*.

The set of integers has all the properties of an ordered field except the
existence of multiplicative inverses. Before defining the set of rational
numbers, defining addition and multiplication for this set, and proving that
the set of rational numbers has the field properties, we shall consider some of
the immediate consequences of the ordered field properties.

THEOREM 3.1   There is only one additive identity in a set with the
field properties.

Proof: Let 0 and 0′ be additive identities.   Then, $0 + 0' = 0$ since
0′ is an additive identity, and $0' + 0 = 0'$ since 0 is an additive identity.
Since $0 + 0' = 0' + 0$, we conclude that $0 = 0'$; thus, the additive identity
is unique.

THEOREM 3.2   There is only one multiplicative identity in a set
with the field properties.

Proof: Left as an exercise for the reader.

THEOREM 3.3   Let x, y, and z be elements in a field.   If
$x + z = y + z$, then $x = y$.

Proof: Let t be an additive inverse of z; thus, $z + t = 0$.   Since
$x + z = y + z$, we have

$$(x + z) + t = (y + z) + t$$

and
$$x + (z + t) = y + (z + t).$$

Hence,
$$x + 0 = y + 0$$

and
$$x = y.$$

THEOREM 3.4   Let x, y, and z be elements in a field.   If $z \neq 0$,
and if $xz = yz$, then $x = y$.

Proof: Left as an exercise for the reader.

THEOREM 3.5   For any element x in a field, there is only one additive inverse of x.

Proof: Assume s and t are additive inverses of x.   Then,

$$x + s = 0$$

and

$$x + t = 0.$$

Thus,

$$x + s = x + t$$

and

$$s = t. \qquad \qquad \text{THEOREM 3.3}$$

THEOREM 3.6   For any $x \neq 0$ in a field, there is only one multiplicative inverse of x.

Proof: Left as an exercise for the reader.

THEOREM 3.7   If x is any element in an ordered field and if $x < 0$, then $-x > 0$ where $-x$ is the unique additive inverse of x.

Proof: If $x < 0$, then $x + (-x) < 0 + (-x)$ as a consequence of the ordered field properties.   Hence, $0 < -x$ and $-x > 0$.

THEOREM 3.8   Let x and y be elements of an ordered field and let $-x$ and $-y$ be their additive inverses, respectively.   If $x < y$, then $-x > -y$.

Proof: Left as an exercise for the reader.

THEOREM 3.9   If x is any element of a field, then $x \cdot 0 = 0$.

Proof: Since $0 + 0 = 0$, $x(0 + 0) = x \cdot 0$.   But, $0 + x \cdot 0 = x \cdot 0$ since 0 is the additive identity.   Thus,

$$x \cdot 0 + x \cdot 0 = 0 + x \cdot 0$$

and

$$x \cdot 0 = 0. \qquad \qquad \text{THEOREM 3.3}$$

THEOREM 3.10   If x and y are elements of a field, then

$$(x)(-y) = -(xy).$$

Proof: Since $y + (-y) = 0$, we conclude that

$$x(y + (-y)) = x \cdot 0.$$

Then, by the distributive property and Theorem 3.9,

$$xy + x(-y) = 0.$$

Since xy is an element of the field, it has an additive inverse $-(xy)$ such that $xy + (-(xy)) = 0.$ Hence,

$$xy + x(-y) = xy + (-(xy)).$$

Consequently, $x(-y) = -(xy)$ by the commutative property of addition and Theorem 3.3.

THEOREM 3.11   Let x, y, and z be elements of an ordered field.

If $x < y$ and $z < 0$, then $xz > yz$.

Proof: If $z < 0$, then $-z > 0$ by Theorem 3.7. If $x < y$ and $-z > 0$, then $x(-z) < y(-z)$.
By Theorem 3.10,

$$-xz < -yz$$

and by Theorem 3.8 we conclude

$$xz > yz.$$

THEOREM 3.12   If $x \neq 0$, then $x^2 > 0$ where $x^2 = x \cdot x$.

Proof: If $x \neq 0$, then $x < 0$ or $x > 0$ by the trichotomy property. If $x < 0$, then $x \cdot x > x \cdot 0$ by Theorem 3.11; thus, $x^2 > 0$. If $x > 0$, then $x \cdot x > x \cdot 0$ by the field properties; thus, $x^2 > 0$.

If we call any element t of an ordered field positive if and only if $t > 0$, then Theorem 3.12 states that the square of any element in an ordered field, except the additive identity, is positive.

THEOREM 3.13   If $xy = 0$, then $x = 0$ or $y = 0$.

Proof: Left as an exercise for the reader.

When we prove that the set of rational numbers has the ordered field properties, it will follow that the set of rationals has all the properties stated in the preceding thirteen theorems. In fact, all the other important properties of the set of rationals can be derived from the ordered field properties.

EXERCISES

1. Prove Theorem 3.2.
2. Prove Theorem 3.4.
3. Prove Theorem 3.6.
4. Prove Theorem 3.8.
5. Prove Theorem 3.13.
6. Let x and y be elements of a field. Prove that $(-x)(-y) = xy$.
7. If 1 is the multiplicative identity and 0 is the additive identity of an ordered field, prove that $1 > 0$.
8. If x is an element of a field and $x \neq 0$, prove that the multiplicative inverse of the multiplicative inverse of x is x.
9. If x is an element of a field, prove that $-(-x) = x$.
10. If $x > 0$, then $y + (-x) < y$ where x and y are elements of an ordered field.

3.2 Addition

Let I be the set of integers and let $S = I \times I$. Then,

$$* = \{((x, y), (u, v)) \quad \text{such that} \quad x, y, u, v \text{ are integers,}$$

$$y \neq 0, \quad v \neq 0, \quad \text{and} \quad xv = yu\}$$

is an equivalence relation on S. See Exercise 4, page 25. The equivalence set $(a, b)^*$ is called a *rational number*; the set of all such equivalence sets is the set of rational numbers. Two equivalence sets $(a, b)^*$ and $(c, d)^*$ are equal if and only if $ad = bc$.

If $(a, b)^*$ and $(c, d)^*$ are two rational numbers, $b \neq 0$, $d \neq 0$ and it follows that $bd \neq 0$; thus, $(ad + bc, bd)^*$ is a rational number. The rational number $(ad + bc, bd)^*$ is called the *sum* of the two given rational numbers; symbolically,

$$(a, b)^* + (c, d)^* = (ad + bc, bd)^*.$$

We prove first that the set of rational numbers has the properties of a field; then, we define an order relation and prove the set has the ordered field properties.

THEOREM 3.14   *Commutative property of addition.*   For every pair of rationals $(a, b)^*$ and $(c, d)^*$,

$$(a, b)^* + (c, d)^* = (c, d)^* + (a, b)^*.$$

Proof: $(a, b)^* + (c, d)^* = (ad + bc, bd)^*$ by definition of addition, and

$$(c, d)^* + (a, b)^* = (cb + da, db)^*.$$

Since

$$(ad + bc)db = (cb + da)bd,$$

it follows that

$$(ad + bc, bd)^* = (cb + da, db)^*;$$

the theorem is proved.

THEOREM 3.15   *Associative property of addition.*   For rationals $(a, b)^*$, $(c, d)^*$, and $(e, f)^*$,

$$[(a, b)^* + (c, d)^*] + (e, f)^* = (a, b)^* + [(c, d)^* + (e, f)^*].$$

Proof: Left as an exercise for the reader.

THEOREM 3.16   *Additive identity.*   For any rational number $(c, d)^*$,

$$(c, d)^* + (0, 1)^* = (c, d)^*.$$

Proof: Left as an exercise for the reader.

THEOREM 3.17   *Additive inverses.*   For any rational number $(a, b)^*$,

$$(a, b)^* + (-a, b)^* = (0, 1)^*.$$

Proof: Left as an exercise for the reader.

EXERCISES

1.   Prove Theorem 3.15.
2.   Prove Theorem 3.16.
3.   Prove Theorem 3.17.
4.   Prove that if $(c, d)^* + (a, b)^* = (c, d)^*$, then $(a, b)^* = (0, 1)^*$.

3.3   Multiplication

Let $(a, b)^*$ and $(c, d)^*$ be two rational numbers.   Since $b \neq 0$ and $d \neq 0$, it follows that $bd \neq 0$ and $(ac, bd)^*$ is a rational number.   The rational number $(ac, bd)^*$ is called the *product* of the two given rational numbers; symbolically,

$$(a, b)^*(c, d)^* = (ac, bd)^*.$$

THEOREM 3.18   *Commutative property of multiplication.*   For every pair of rational numbers $(a, b)^*$ and $(c, d)^*$,

$$(a, b)^*(c, d)^* = (c, d)^*(a, b)^*.$$

Proof: $(a, b)^*(c, d)^* = (ac, bd)^*$ by definition, and $(c, d)^*(a, b) = (ca, db)^*$. Since $(ac, bd)^* = (ca, db)^*$, the theorem is proved.

THEOREM 3.19   *Associative property of multiplication.*   For rationals $(a, b)^*$, $(c, d)^*$, and $(e, f)^*$,

$$[(a, b)^*(c, d)^*](e, f)^* = (a, b)^*[(c, d)^*(e, f)^*].$$

Proof: Left as an exercise for the reader.

THEOREM 3.20   *Multiplicative identity.*   For any rational number $(c, d)^*$,

$$(c, d)^*(1, 1)^* = (c, d)^*.$$

Proof: Left as an exercise for the reader.

THEOREM 3.21   *Multiplicative inverses.*   For any rational number $(a, b)^*$ different from $(0, 1)^*$, the rational $(b, a)^*$ has the property that $(a, b)^*(b, a)^* = (1, 1)^*$.

Proof: Left as an exercise for the reader.

THEOREM 3.22   *Distributive property.*   For rational numbers $(a, b)^*$, $(c, d)^*$, and $(e, f)^*$,

$$(a, b)^*[(c, d) + (e, f)^*] = (a, b)^*(c, d)^* + (a, b)^*(e, f)^*.$$

Proof: Left as an exercise for the reader.

Since the set of rational numbers has the properties of a field, we often refer to the set as the *rational field*.   Our next step is to define an order relation for the set of rational numbers and prove that the set has the properties of an ordered field.

3.4   Order

We define a rational number $(a, b)^*$ to be *positive* if and only if $ab > 0$. As a consequence of Theorem 3.7 and the fact that $(a, b)^* =$

$(-a, -b)^*$, we may assume without loss of generality that $a > 0$ and $b > 0$ if $(a, b)^*$ is a positive rational number. With this assumption and the definitions of addition and multiplication for rational numbers, it is quite easy to prove that the sum, or product, of two positive rational numbers is a positive rational number.

THEOREM 3.23 Let $(a, b)^*$ and $(c, d)^*$ be positive rational numbers. Then, $(a, b)^* + (c, d)^*$ and $(a, b)^*(c, d)^*$ are positive rational numbers.

Proof: Left as an exercise for the reader.

The less than relation is defined for rational numbers in the following manner. $(a, b)^*$ is *less than* $(c, d)^*$, denoted by $(a, b)^* < (c, d)^*$, if and only if there exists a positive rational number $(x, y)^*$ such that

$$(a, b)^* + (x, y)^* = (c, d)^*.$$

THEOREM 3.24 *Trichotomy property.* For any pair of rational numbers $(a, b)^*$ and $(c, d)^*$, one and only one of the following is true: (1) $(a, b)^* < (c, d)^*$, (2) $(a, b)^* = (c, d)^*$, or (3) $(a, b)^* > (c, d)^*$.

Proof: Part 1. We first show that at most one of statements (1), (2), (3) is true. Let $x = (a, b)^*$ and $y = (c, d)^*$.

A. Assume that both (1) and (2) are true. If $x < y$, then there is a positive rational s such that $x + s = y$. If $x = y$, then $x + s = x$; by Exercise 4, page 31, $s = (0, 1)^*$, which contradicts the fact that s is positive. Hence, both (1) and (2) cannot be true.

B. Assuming (2) and (3) to be true leads to a contradiction similar to that in A.

C. Assume that (1) and (3) are true. Then, $x + s = y$, where s is positive, and $x = y + t$, where t is a positive rational. Consequently,

$$(y + t) + s = y$$
$$y + (t + s) = y.$$

Since t and s are positive, $t + s$ is positive, and we again have a contradiction. Hence, both (1) and (3) cannot be true.

Part 2. We now prove that at least one of the statements is true. If $(a, b)^* = (c, d)^*$, then the theorem is true. Thus, we need to show that $(a, b)^* \neq (c, d)^*$ implies that $(a, b)^* < (c, d)^*$ or $(a, b)^* > (c, d)^*$. We assume without loss of generality that $bd > 0$.

If $(a, b)^* \neq (c, d)^*$, then $ad \neq bc$ and either $ad < bc$ or $ad > bc$. Assume that $ad < bc$. Thus, $ad + x = bc$, where x is a positive integer. Multiplying by bd, we get

$$abd^2 + bdx + b^2cd.$$

By definition of equality for rational numbers, it follows that

$$(abd + bx, b^2d)^* = (c, d)^*.$$

Now $(x, bd)^*$ is positive since $xbd > 0$. Furthermore,

$$(a, b)^* + (x, bd)^* = (abd + bx, b^2d)^* = (c, d)^*.$$

Hence, $(a, b)^* < (c, d)^*.$

We leave as an exercise for the reader to prove that $bd > 0$ and $ad > bc$ implies $(a, b)^* > (c, d)^*$.

THEOREM 3.25 *Transitive property of less than relation.* If $(a, b)^* < (c, d)^*$ and $(c, d)^* < (e, f)^*$, then $(a, b)^* < (e, f)^*$.

Proof: If $(a, b)^* < (c, d)^*$, then there is a positive rational $(x, y)^*$ such that $(a, b)^* + (x, y)^* = (c, d)^*$. Similarly, there is a positive rational $(u, v)^*$ such that $(c, d)^* + (u, v)^* = (e, f)^*$. Hence,

$$[(a, b)^* + (x, y)^*] + (u, v)^* = (e, f)^*.$$

Thus, $(a, b)^* + [(x, y)^* + (u, v)^*] = (e, f)^*$ by the associative property of addition. Since the sum of two positive rational numbers is a positive rational number, $(x, y)^* + (u, v)^*$ is positive and $(a, b)^* < (e, f)^*$ by definition of the less than relation.

Theorems 3.24 and 3.25 prove that the set of rational numbers is an ordered set. The following three theorems complete our task of proving that the set of rational numbers has the ordered field properties.

THEOREM 3.26   If $(a, b)^* < (c, d)^*$, then $(a, b)^* + (x, y)^* < (c, d)^* + (x, y)^*$ for any rational number $(x, y)^*$.

Proof: If $(a, b)^* < (c, d)^*$, then there is a positive rational number $(u, v)^*$ such that $(a, b)^* + (u, v)^* = (c, d)^*$. Hence,

$$[(a, b)^* + (u, v)^*] + (x, y)^* = (c, d)^* + (x, y)^*,$$

and $[(a, b)^* + (x, y)^*] + (u, v)^* = (c, d)^* + (x, y)^*.$

Since $(u, v)^*$ is positive,

$$(a, b)^* + (x, y) < (c, d)^* + (x, y)^*.$$

THEOREM 3.27 $(a, b)^* > (0, 1)^*$ if and only if $(a, b)^*$ is a positive rational number.

Proof: Left as an exercise for the reader.

THEOREM 3.28 If $(a, b)^* < (c, d)^*$ and $(x, y)^* > (0, 1)^*$, then $(a, b)^*(x, y)^* < (c, d)^*(x, y)^*$.

Proof: Since $(x, y)^* > (0, 1)^*$, $(x, y)^*$ is a positive rational by Theorem 3.27. Since $(a, b)^* < (c, d)^*$, then there is a positive rational $(u, v)^*$ such that $(a, b)^* + (u, v)^* = (c, d)^*$. Thus,

$$[(a, b)^* + (u, v)^*] \cdot (x, y)^* = (c, d)^*(x, y)^*,$$

and $(a, b)^*(x, y)^* + (u, v)^*(x, y)^* = (c, d)^*(x, y)^*$. The product $(u, v)^*(x, y)^*$ is a positive rational number since $(u, v)^*$ and $(x, y)^*$ are positive; thus,

$$(a, b)^*(x, y)^* < (c, d)^*(x, y)^*.$$

EXERCISES

1. Prove Theorem 3.19.
2. Prove Theorem 3.20.
3. Prove Theorem 3.21.
4. Prove Theorem 3.22.
5. Prove Theorem 3.23.
6. Prove Theorem 3.27.
7. Consider the set of rational numbers $(a, 1)^*$ where a is an integer. Prove that this set is isomorphic to the set of integers.
8. Complete the proof to Theorem 3.24 by proving that $bd > 0, (a, b)^* \neq (c, d)^*$, and $ad > bc$ implies $(a, b)^* > (c, d)^*$.
9. (a) Let s be a rational where $s > 0$. Prove there exists a rational p such that $ps > 1$. Note: "0" is the additive identity $(0, 1)^*$ and "1" is the multiplicative identity $(1, 1)^*$.
    (b) If s, t are rationals such that $s > t$ and $t > 0$, prove there is a rational number r such that $rt > s$.
10. Prove there is no rational number $(x, y)^*$ such that $(x, y)^*(x, y)^* = (2, 1)^*$.

4   THE REAL NUMBERS

4.1 Introduction

Although we have not discussed fractions, decimals, and mixed numerals, we assume the reader is already familiar with these notations for rational numbers and with the techniques for doing arithmetical calculations with rationals using each notation. Furthermore, we assume a familiarity with such facts concerning the rational numbers as the following: If a and b are rational numbers and if $a < b$, then $a < (a + b)/2$ and $(a + b)/2 < b$; that is, $a < (a + b)/2 < b$. In other words, the arithmetic mean of two rational numbers is a rational number between the two given rationals.

Throughout this chapter, we use lower case Latin letters to denote rational numbers, Greek letters to denote real numbers, and Q to denote the set of rational numbers. One goal is to define the set of real numbers, define order on the set, and then prove the set has the ordered field properties.

4.2 Order

A real number α is a set of rational numbers with the following properties.

I. α is a non-empty set of rational numbers and its complement relative to Q is non-empty. In other words, there is at least one rational number in the set α and at least one rational number not in α.

II. If s is in α and if $x < s$, then x is in α. In other words, if s is a rational in the set α, then every rational less than s is in α.

III. If s is in α, then there is at least one rational number t such that $t > s$ and t is in α. In other words, the set α does not contain a largest rational number.

EXAMPLES

1. If $\alpha = \{x$ such that x is a rational number and $x < 7\}$, then α is a real number. The proof follows.
    I. By definition of α, 0 is in α so α is not empty. Furthermore, 8 is not in α so the complement of α is not empty.
    II. If s is in α, then s is rational and $s < 7$ by definition of α. If x is a rational number such that $x < s$, then $x < 7$ and x is in α.
    III. If s is a rational in α, then $s < 7$. Let $t = (s + 7)/2$. Now, $s < (s + 7)/2 < 7$; thus, $t > s$ and t is in α since $t < 7$.
    Consequently, α is a real number.

2. Let $\beta = \{x$ such that x is rational, $x \le 0$ or $x > 0$ and $x^2 < 3\}$. Then β is a real number. The proof follows.
    I. Since 0 is in β, β is not empty. Since $2^2 > 3$, 2 is a rational number not in β and the complement of β is not empty.
    II. If s is in β, then $s \le 0$ or $s > 0$ and $s^2 < 3$. If $x < s$ and $s \le 0$, then $x < 0$ and x is in β. If $x < s$ and $s > 0$, then either $x \le 0$ or $x > 0$; if $x \le 0$, x is in β. If $0 < x < s$, $x^2 < s^2$ and x is in β.
    III. Let s be in β. If $s \le 0$, then there exists a rational number t in β greater than s, namely $t = 1$.

    (A) If $s > 0$, let $t = 6s/(s^2 + 3)$. (We want to prove that $t > s$ and $t^2 < 3$.)

    $$t - s = \frac{6s}{s^2 + 3} - s$$

    $$= \frac{6s - s^3 - 3s}{s^2 + 3}$$

    $$= \frac{s(3 - s^2)}{s^2 + 3} > 0 \quad \text{since } s > 0 \text{ and } s^2 < 3.$$

    Hence, $s < t$.

    (B) $\quad 3 - t^2 = 3 - \left(\frac{6s}{s^2 + 3}\right)^2$

    $$= 3 - \frac{36s^2}{(s^2 + 3)^2}$$

    $$= \frac{3[(s^2 + 3)^2 - 12s^2]}{(s^2 + 3)^2}$$

    $$= \frac{3(s^2 - 3)^2}{(s^2 + 3)^2} > 0 \quad \text{since } s^2 \ne 0.$$

    Hence, $t^2 < 3$. Consequently, β is a real number.

EXERCISES

1. Is $\gamma = \{x$ such that $x \leq 0$ or $x > 0$ and $x^2 < 2\}$ a real number? Justify. Hint: See Example 2.
2. Is $\delta = \{x$ such that x is in Q and $x \leq 5\}$ a real number? Justify.
3. Prove that $\lambda = \{x$ such x is in Q and $x^3 < 5\}$ is a real number? Hint: For part III, if $s > 0$ let $t = 15s/(s^3 + 10)$.
4. Is $\phi = \{x$ such that x is rational and $x^2 < 5\}$ a real number? Justify.
5. Prove that if a is a rational number, then

    $$\alpha = \{x \text{ such that } x \text{ is in } Q \text{ and } x < a\} \text{ is a real number.}$$

6. Prove that if β is a real number, s is in β, and x is not in β, then $x > s$.
7. Let α be a real number. Prove that if $s > t$ for every t in α, then s is not in α.
8. Let α be a real number. If s is not in α, then $s > t$ for every t in α.
9. Let α be a real number and let s be a positive rational. Prove there are rationals p in α and q not in α where q is not the least rational in the complement of α and $q + (-p) = s$. Hint: Let x be in α and let $t_n = x + ns$. By Exercise 9, page 35, there is an integer n such that $x + ns > u$ where u is in the complement of α.

If α and β are real numbers, then $\alpha = \beta$ means set equality. To prove two real numbers α and β are equal, we need to show that every rational in α is in β and that every rational in β is in α.

If a real number α is a proper subset of a real number β (every rational in α is in β and β has at least one rational number not in α), we say that α is *less than* β and denote this by $\alpha < \beta$. Similarly, if β is a proper subset of α, β is less than α. As we did previously, we define $\alpha > \beta$ (α greater than β) if and only if $\beta < \alpha$; furthermore, $\alpha \leq \beta$ if and only if $\alpha < \beta$ or $\alpha = \beta$.

THEOREM 4.1 *Trichotomy property.* Let α and β be real numbers. One and only one of the following is true: $\alpha < \beta$, $\alpha = \beta$, $\alpha > \beta$.

Proof: Part 1. It follows from the definition of equality of sets and the definition of subset that at most one is true.

Part 2. If $\alpha = \beta$, then at least one is true and the theorem is proved. Thus, assume that $\alpha \neq \beta$. Either there is a rational number x in α and not in β or there is a rational number y in β and not in α.

Assume x is in α and x is not in β. Let s be any rational number in β. Then, $s < x$. (See Exercise 8, page 38). Since α is a real number and x is in α and $s < x$, we conclude that s is in α. Hence, every rational in β is in α and $\beta < \alpha$.

Similarly, if y is in β and not in α, we can prove $\alpha < \beta$. This is left as an exercise for the reader.

THEOREM 4.2   *Transitive property.*   Let α, β, and γ be real numbers, If $\alpha < \beta$ and $\beta < \gamma$, then $\alpha < \gamma$.

Proof: Since $\alpha < \beta$, for any rational number x in α, we conclude x is in β.   Since $\beta < \gamma$, we conclude x is also in γ.   Consequently, every rational number in α is in γ; thus, $\alpha \leq \gamma$.   Furthermore, since $\beta < \gamma$, there is a rational number y in γ that is not in β.   If y were in α, then $\alpha < \beta$ would imply that y was in β; thus, y is not in α.   Hence, $\alpha < \gamma$.

From Theorem 4.1 and 4.2, we conclude that the set of real numbers is an ordered set.

4.3   Addition

THEOREM 4.3   Let α and β be real numbers.   Let γ be the set of rationals defined by

$$\gamma = \{x + y \text{ such that } x \text{ is in } \alpha \text{ and } y \text{ is in } \beta\}.$$

Then, γ is a real number.

Proof: We need to prove that γ has properties I, II, and III.
   I.   Since α and β are real numbers, there is a rational x in α and a rational number y in β.   Thus, the rational $x + y$ is in γ by definition of γ.
   Since α and β are real numbers, there is a rational s not in α and a rational t not in β.   By Exercise 8, page 38, $s > x$ for every x in α and $t > y$ for every y in β.   Consequently, $s + t > x + y$ for every $x + y$ in γ. Hence, $s + t$ is not in γ.
   II.   If s is in α, then $s = x + y$ where x is in α and y is in β.   If $t < s$, then $t + m = s$ where $m > 0$.   Thus, $t + m = x + y$ and $t = x + [y + (-m)]$, Now, $y + (-m) < y$ which implies $y + (-m)$ is in β.   Since x is in α, t is in γ by definition of γ.
   III.   If s is in γ, then $s = x + y$ where x is in α and y is in β.   Since α is a real number, there is a rational number t such that $t > x$ and t is in α. Furthermore, $t + y > x + y = s$.   Thus, $t + y$ is a rational number in γ greater than s.

As a consequence of proving γ has properties I, II, and III, we conclude that γ is a real number.

If α and β are real numbers, then the real number γ defined in Theorem 4.3 is called the *sum* of α and β. Symbolically, $\alpha + \beta = \gamma$.

THEOREM 4.4 *Commutative property of addition.* If α and β are real numbers, then $\alpha + \beta = \beta + \alpha$.

Proof: By definition of addition,

$$\alpha + \beta = \{x + y \text{ such that } x \text{ is in } \alpha \text{ and } y \text{ is in } \beta\}$$

and

$$\beta + \alpha = \{y + x \text{ such that } y \text{ is in } \beta \text{ and } x \text{ is in } \alpha\}.$$

Since $x + y = y + x$ for rational numbers, $\alpha + \beta = \beta + \alpha$.

THEOREM 4.5 *Associative property of addition.* If α, β, and γ are real numbers, then $(\alpha + \beta) + \gamma = \alpha + (\beta + \gamma)$.

Proof: Left as an exercise for the reader.

THEOREM 4.6 *Additive identity.* Let $\bar{0}$ be the real number defined by $\bar{0} = \{x \text{ such that } x \text{ is rational and } x < 0\}$. For any real number α, $\alpha + \bar{0} = \alpha$.

Proof: We need to prove that every rational number in $\alpha + \bar{0}$ is in α and every rational number in α is in $\alpha + \bar{0}$.

Part 1. If t is any rational in $\alpha + \bar{0}$, then $t = x + y$ where x is in α and y is in $\bar{0}$. By definition of $\bar{0}$, $y < 0$; hence, $x + y < x$. Now, α is a real number, x is in α, and $t = x + y < x$; hence, t is in α and $\alpha + \bar{0} \leq \alpha$.

Part 2. If t is any rational number in α, there is a rational number s in α such that $s > t$. Hence, $s = t + m$ where $m > 0$. Consequently,

$$t = s + (-m) \quad \text{where} \quad (-m) < 0.$$

Since s is in α and $(-m)$ is in $\bar{0}$, then t is in $\alpha + \bar{0}$; thus, $\alpha \leq \alpha + \bar{0}$. The theorem is proved.

Let α be a real number and consider the set of all rational numbers not in α; this set is the complement of α relative to Q and is denoted by $C(\alpha)$. If $C(\alpha)$ contains a least rational number t, then the set of all rational numbers in the complement $C(\alpha)$ except this least number t is called the *deleted complement of* α and is denoted by $C'(\alpha)$. If $C(\alpha)$ does not contain a least rational number, we define $C'(\alpha)$ to be equal to $C(\alpha)$. For example, if $\alpha = \{x \text{ such that } x < 7\}$, then $C(\alpha) = \{x \text{ such that } x \geq 7\}$ and $C'(\alpha) = \{x \text{ such that } x > 7\}$. If $\beta = \{x \text{ such that } x^3 < 5\}$, then $C(\alpha) = \{x \text{ such that } x^3 > 5\}$ since there is no rational number x such that $x^3 = 5$. In this case, $C'(\alpha) = C(\alpha)$.

THEOREM 4.7 Let α be a real number. If $(-\alpha)$ is the set of rational numbers defined by $(-\alpha) = \{x \text{ such that } -x \text{ is in } C'(\alpha)\}$, then $(-\alpha)$ is a real number.

Proof: Before proving that $(-\alpha)$ has properties I, II, and III, let us note that if t is in $C'(\alpha)$, then $-t$ is in $(-\alpha)$ from the definition of $(-\alpha)$.

I. Since α is a real number, there is a rational number s in $C(\alpha)$. Hence, $t = s + 1$ is in $C'(\alpha)$ and $-t$ is in $(-\alpha)$ by definition of $(-\alpha)$.

Since α is a real number, there is a rational t in α. But t is not in $C'(\alpha)$; thus, $-t$ is not in $(-\alpha)$.

II. Let s be any rational number in $(-\alpha)$ and let $x < s$. By definition of $(-\alpha)$, $-s$ is in $C'(\alpha)$. Since $-x > -s$, we conclude that $-x$ is in $C'(\alpha)$; thus, x is in $(-\alpha)$.

III. Let s be any rational number in $(-\alpha)$; thus, $-s$ is in $C'(\alpha)$. Since $C'(\alpha)$ does not contain a least rational number, there is a rational $-t$ in $C'(\alpha)$ such that $-t < -s$. Hence, t is in $(-\alpha)$ and $t > s$.

THEOREM 4.8 *Additive inverses.* For any real number α, $(-\alpha)$ is the real number such that $\alpha + (-\alpha) = \bar{0}$.

Proof: We need to prove that every rational number in $\alpha + (-\alpha)$ is in $\bar{0}$ and every rational number in $\bar{0}$ is in $\alpha + (-\alpha)$.

Part 1. If t is any rational in $\alpha + (-\alpha)$, then $t = x + y$ where x is in α and y is in $(-\alpha)$. Since y is in $(-\alpha)$, we conclude $-y$ is in $C'(\alpha)$; thus, $-y > x$. Consequently, $0 > x + y$ and t is in $\bar{0}$. Hence, $\alpha + (-\alpha) \leq \bar{0}$.

Part 2. If s is any rational in $\bar{0}$, then $s < 0$ and $-s > 0$. By Exercise 9, page 38, there exist rationals p and q such that p is in α, q is in $C'(\alpha)$, and $q + (-p) = -s$. Since q is in $C'(\alpha)$, $-q$ is in $(-\alpha)$. Thus, $s = p + (-q)$ and s is in $\alpha + (-\alpha)$. Hence, $\bar{0} \leq \alpha + (-\alpha)$ and the theorem is proved.

If α is a real number such that $\alpha > \bar{0}$, then α is called *positive*; if $\alpha < \bar{0}$, then α is called *negative*. The set of real numbers less than or equal to $\bar{0}$ is called the set of non-positive real numbers and the set of real numbers greater than or equal to $\bar{0}$ is called the non-negative real numbers.

EXERCISES

1. Let *a* be any rational number. The real number defined by $\bar{a} = \{x$ such that $x < a\}$ is called a *rational real*. Prove that if $\bar{a}$ and $\bar{b}$ are rational reals such that $\bar{a} < \bar{b}$, then there exists a rational real $\bar{c}$ such that $\bar{a} < \bar{c}$ and $\bar{c} < \bar{b}$.
2. Let $\bar{2}, \bar{3}$, and $\bar{5}$ be rational reals as defined in Exercise 1. Prove that $\bar{2} + \bar{3} = \bar{5}$.
3. If α is a positive real, prove that there is a positive rational x in α.
4. Prove Theorem 4.5.
5. Prove that if α and β are real numbers, and if there is a y in β and y is not in α, then $\alpha < \beta$.
6. Prove that if γ_1 and γ_2 are two real numbers such that $\gamma_1 < \gamma_2$, then there exists a rational real γ such that $\gamma_1 < \gamma < \gamma_2$.
7. Prove that $\alpha < \bar{0}$ if and only if $(-\alpha) > \bar{0}$.

4.4 Multiplication

THEOREM 4.9 Let α and β be *positive real numbers*. Let $\gamma = \{x$ such that $x \leq 0$ or $x = pq$ where $p > 0, q > 0, p$ is in α, and q is in $\beta\}$. Then, γ is a real number.

Proof: I. By definition of γ, 0 is in γ. Since α is a real number, there exists a positive rational s such that $s > x$ for every x in α; similarly, there exists a positive rational t such that $t > y$ for every y in β. Thus, $st > xy$ and st is not in γ.

II. We need to show that if r is in γ and $z < r$, z is in γ. If $r \leq 0$ and $z < r$, then $z < 0$ and z is in γ. If $r > 0$, we may assume that $0 < z < r$ since every $z \leq 0$ is in γ; furthermore, $r = pq$ where p is a positive rational in α and q is a positive rational in β. Since $z < pq, \dfrac{z}{p} < q$ and $\dfrac{z}{p}$ is in β. Since p is in α, $z = p\left(\dfrac{z}{p}\right)$ is in γ.

III. We need to show that if s is in γ, there is a rational number t such that $t > s$ is in γ. If $s < 0$, let $t = 0$; in this case, $t > s$ and t is in γ.

Assume $s = 0$. Since α and β are positive real numbers, there are positive rationals u in α and v in γ. Thus, $z = uv > s$ and z is in γ.

Assume $s > 0$. Then $s = pq$ where p is a positive rational in α and q is a positive rational in β. Since α is a real number, there is a positive rational t in α such that $t > p$. Hence, $tq > pq$ and $z = tq$ is a rational number in γ greater than s. The theorem is proved.

If α and β are *positive real numbers*, then the number defined in Theorem 4.9 is called the *product* of α and β. Symbolically, $\alpha\beta = \gamma$.

THEOREM 4.10   *Commutative property of multiplication.*   If α and β are positive real numbers, then $\alpha\beta = \beta\alpha$.

Proof: Left as an exercise for the reader.

THEOREM 4.11   *Associative property of multiplication.*   If α, β, and γ are positive real numbers, then

$$\alpha(\beta\gamma) = (\alpha\beta)\gamma.$$

Proof: Left as an exercise for the reader.

THEOREM 4.12   *Multiplicative identity.*   Let $\bar{1}$ be the real number defined by $\bar{1} = \{x \text{ such that } x < 1\}$. For any positive real number α, $\alpha \cdot \bar{1} = \alpha$.

Proof: Part 1.   Let x be any rational in $\alpha \cdot \bar{1}$. If $x \leq 0$, then x is in α by definition. If $x > 0$, then $x = pq$ where p is a positive rational in α and q is a positive rational in $\bar{1}$. Thus, $0 < q < 1$ and $pq < p$. Hence, $x = pq$ is in α, and every rational in $\alpha \cdot \bar{1}$ is in α and $\alpha \cdot \bar{1} \subseteq \alpha$.

Part 2.   Let s be any rational in α. If $s \leq 0$, then s is in $\alpha \cdot \bar{1}$. If $s > 0$, there is a rational number $t > s$ such that t is in α. Hence, $\frac{s}{t} < 1$ and $\frac{s}{t}$ is in $\bar{1}$. Since t is in α and since $s = t\left(\frac{s}{t}\right)$, s is in $\alpha \cdot \bar{1}$. Thus, $\alpha \subseteq \alpha \cdot \bar{1}$.

THEOREM 4.13   Let α be a positive real number. Let α^{-1} be the set of rational numbers defined by $\alpha^{-1} = \{x \text{ such that } x \leq 0 \text{ or } x > 0 \text{ and } 1/x \text{ is in } C'(\alpha)\}$. Then, α^{-1} is a real number.

Proof: I.   Since 0 is in α^{-1}, the set is not empty. Since α is positive, there is some positive rational number s in α. Hence, s is not in $C'(\alpha)$. Thus, $1/s$ is not in α^{-1}.

II.   Let t be a rational in α^{-1}. If $t \leq 0$ and $s < t$, then s is in α^{-1}. If $t > 0$, then $1/t$ is in $C'(\alpha)$. But, $1/s > 1/t$ if $s < t$. Hence $1/s$ is in $C'(\alpha)$ and s is in α^{-1}.

III.   Since α is positive, there is a positive rational not only in α but also in α^{-1}. Thus, if t is in α^{-1} and if $t \leq 0$, then there is a (positive) rational $s > t$ such that s is in α^{-1}. If t is in α^{-1} and $t > 0$, then $1/t$ is in $C'(\alpha)$. Since $C'(\alpha)$ does not contain a smallest number, let $1/s$ be a rational in $C'(\alpha)$ where $1/s < 1/t$. Hence, $s > t$, and s is in α^{-1}.

THEOREM 4.14 *Multiplicative inverses.* If α is a positive real number, then α^{-1} is the real number such that $\alpha \cdot \alpha^{-1} = \bar{1}$.

Proof: Part 1. Let x be any rational number in $\alpha \cdot \alpha^{-1}$. If $x \leq 0$, then x is in $\bar{1}$. If $x > 0$, then $x = pq$ where $p > 0$, $q > 0$, p is in α, and q is in α^{-1}. Since q is in α^{-1}, $1/q$ is in $C'(\alpha)$; thus,

$$p < 1/q.$$

Consequently, $pq < 1$ and $x = pq$ is in $\bar{1}$. Hence, $\alpha \cdot \alpha^{-1} \leq \bar{1}$.

Part 2. Let x be any rational number in $\bar{1}$. If $x \leq 0$, then x is in $\alpha \cdot \alpha^{-1}$. Assume $0 < x < 1$. Hence, $1 - x > 0$. Let a be any positive rational number in α; then, $a(1 - x) > 0$. From Exercise 9, page 38 there exist rationals p and q such that p is in α, q is in $C'(\alpha)$, and

$$q - p = a(1 - x).$$

Since q is in $C'(\alpha)$, $a < q$ and $a(1 - x) < q(1 - x)$.

Consequently, $\qquad\qquad q - p < q(1 - x)$

and $\qquad\qquad\qquad q - p < q - qx.$

Thus, $\qquad\qquad\qquad\qquad qx < p$

and $\qquad\qquad\qquad\qquad q < \dfrac{p}{x}.$

Since $p/x > q$, p/x is in $C'(\alpha)$ and x/p is in α^{-1}. Now, p is in α so $p(x/p) = x$ is in $\alpha \cdot \alpha^{-1}$. Therefore, $\bar{1} \leq \alpha \cdot \alpha^{-1}$ and the theorem is proved.

THEOREM 4.15 If α, β, and γ are positive real numbers, then

$$\alpha(\beta + \gamma) = \alpha\beta + \alpha\gamma.$$

Proof: Left as an exercise for the reader.

We have proved that the set of real numbers has all the additive properties of a field. Since multiplication was only defined for positive real numbers, we only proved that the set of positive real numbers has the multiplicative properties of a field. We now define multiplication for all real numbers and leave as an exercise for the reader the completion of the proof that the set of real numbers has the field properties.

Let α and β be real numbers. Then, we *define*

$$\alpha\beta = \bar{0} \quad \text{if} \quad \alpha = \bar{0} \quad \text{or} \quad \beta = \bar{0}.$$

$\alpha\beta$ is defined by Theorem 4.9 if $\alpha > \bar{0}$ and $\beta > \bar{0}$.

$$\alpha\beta = -[(-\alpha)(\beta)] \quad \text{if } \alpha < \bar{0} \quad \text{and} \quad \beta > \bar{0}.\dagger$$

$$\alpha\beta = -[(\alpha)(-\beta)] \quad \text{if } \alpha > \bar{0} \quad \text{and} \quad \beta < \bar{0}.$$

$$\alpha\beta = (-\alpha)(-\beta) \quad \text{if } \alpha < \bar{0} \quad \text{and} \quad \beta < \bar{0}.$$

EXERCISES

1. Let $\bar{2}$, $\bar{3}$, and $\bar{6}$ be rational reals. Prove that $\bar{2} \cdot \bar{3} = \bar{6}$.
2. State and prove the theorems that remain to show the set of real numbers has the field properties.

4.5 Ordered Field Properties

THEOREM 4.16 If α and β are real numbers and if $\alpha < \beta$, then $\alpha + \gamma < \beta + \gamma$ for any real number γ.

Proof: Since $\alpha < \beta$, there is a rational p in β such that p is not in α. Choose $q > p$ such that q is in β. Since $q - p = t > 0$, there are rationals r and s such that r is in γ and s is not in γ and $s - r = t$ by Exercise 9, page 38. Thus,

$$s - r = q - p$$

and $$q + r = p + s.$$

Since r is in γ and q is in β, $q + r$ is in $\beta + \gamma$. Since s is not in γ and p is not in α, $p + s > u + v$ for every u in α and v in γ. Thus, $p + s$ is not in $\alpha + \gamma$. Consequently, $r + q$ is not in $\alpha + \gamma$ and $\alpha + \gamma < \beta + \gamma$.

THEOREM 4.17 If α, β, and γ are positive real numbers and $\alpha < \beta$, then $\alpha\gamma < \beta\gamma$.

Proof: We need to prove that there is a rational in $\beta\gamma$ not in $\alpha\gamma$.

Since $\bar{0} < \alpha < \beta$ there is a positive rational p in β and not in α. Let q be a rational in β where $q > p$. Let c be any positive rational in γ and let

$$c_n = c\left(\frac{q}{p}\right)^{n-1}.$$

---

† If $\alpha < \bar{0}$, then $(-\alpha) > \bar{0}$ by Exercise 7, page 42, and the product $(-\alpha)(\beta)$ is defined by Theorem 4.9. $-[(-\alpha)(\beta)]$ is the additive inverse of this product.

There is an integer m such that c_m is in γ and c_{m+1} is not in γ. Furthermore,

$$\frac{c_{m+1}}{c_m} = \frac{q}{p}$$

and

$$pc_{m+1} = qc_m.$$

Since p is not in α, $p > u$ for all u in α. Since c_{m+1} is not in γ, $c_{m+1} > v$ for all v in γ. Thus, $pc_{m+1} > uv$ for any rational uv in $\alpha\gamma$ and pc_{m+1} is not in $\alpha\gamma$. Hence, $c_m q$ is not in $\alpha\gamma$. Since qc_m is in $\beta\gamma$, $\alpha\gamma < \beta\gamma$.

When we prove that Theorem 4.17 is true without restricting α and β to be positive real numbers, we shall have completed proving that the set of real numbers has the ordered field properties. This will be left as an exercise for the reader.

We complete this section on the real numbers by stating and proving what is called the Dedekind Theorem; this theorem is named for the German mathematician Richard Dedekind (1831–1916).

THEOREM 4.18   *Dedekind Theorem.*   Let S be a set of real numbers such that the following are true.

(1)   There is a real number in S and a real number not in S.
(2)   If λ is in S and $\mu < \lambda$, then μ is in S.

Conclusion: There exists one and only one real number γ such that $\alpha < \gamma$ implies α is in S and $\beta > \gamma$ implies β is not in S.

Proof: Part 1.   We first prove that at most one such γ can exist. If two real numbers γ_1 and γ_2 having the stated properties exist, we may assume that $\gamma_1 < \gamma_2$. Thus, by Exercise 6, page 42, there is a rational real γ such that $\gamma_1 < \gamma < \gamma_2$. Since $\gamma_1 < \gamma$, we conclude from (2) that γ is not in S; however, since $\gamma < \gamma_2$, we also conclude from (2) that γ is in S, a contradiction. Hence, if such a real number γ exists, it must be unique.

Part 2.   Let γ be the set of rational numbers defined by the following.

$$\gamma = \{x \text{ such that } x \text{ is in } \alpha \text{ for some real number } \alpha \text{ in } S\}.$$

In other words, a rational number is in γ if it is a member of at least one of the real numbers in S. We must first prove that γ is a real number and then prove that if $\alpha < \gamma$ then α is in S and if $\beta > \gamma$ then β is not in S.

I.   Since S contains at least one real number α, any rational in α is in γ by definition of γ. Let ϕ be any real number not in S; let q be a rational number not in ϕ. Hence, q is not in γ; for if q is in γ, then q is in α for some α in S and $\alpha < \phi$, a contradiction.

II. If p is any rational in γ, then p is in α for some α in S. If $q < p$, then q is in α and q is in γ.

III. Suppose p is in γ. Then there is a real number in S such that p is in α. Let q be a rational in α such that $q > p$. Hence, q is in γ. We conclude that γ is a real number.

Take any $\alpha < \gamma$. Then, there is a rational p in γ such that p is not in α. Since p is in γ, we have p is in β for some β in S. Now, p not in α and p in β implies $\alpha < \beta$. Since β is in S, α is in S.

Take any $\beta > \gamma$. There is a rational p such that p is in β and p is not in γ. If β is in S, we would have p in γ, a contradiction. Hence, β is not in S. The theorem is proved.

Properties 1 and 2, given in the hypotheses of Theorem 4.18, are called the Dedekind properties. Thus, any set S of real numbers with the Dedekind properties defines a real number γ such that $\alpha < \gamma$ implies that α is in S and $\beta > \gamma$ implies β is not in S.

EXERCISES

1. State and prove the theorems remaining to show that the set of real numbers has the ordered field properties.
2. If $\bar{2} = \{x$ such that x is rational and $x < 2\}$, prove that there exists a unique positive real number γ such that $\gamma^2 = \bar{2}$.

4.6 Completeness Property

Both the set of real numbers and the set of rational numbers have the properties of an ordered field. Now, let us consider important differences between these two ordered fields. First, there is a subset of the set of real numbers (namely, the set of rational real numbers) that is an ordered field; however, no subset of the set of rational numbers exists with the properties of an ordered field. Second, the set of real numbers has what is called the completeness property; the set of rational numbers does not have this property. We now consider this important distinguishing property of the set of real numbers.

Let S be any set of numbers having the properties of an ordered field. Suppose there exists a number t such that $x \leq t$ for every x in S; then, the number t is called an *upper bound* for the set S. For example, if S is the set with elements $2/3$, 10, -3, and 26, then, since every number in S is less than, say, 38, we conclude that 38 is an upper bound of S. Of course, 101, 32.25, and 26 are also upper bounds of S. If T is the set of real numbers x such that $x < 3$, then any real number greater than or equal to 3 is an upper bound of T.   If W is the set of real numbers x such that $x \leq 3$, then any real number greater than or equal to 3 is an upper bound of W.   Note that the set of upper bounds for the two different sets T and W is the same.

If the set of upper bounds of a set S has a least number z in it, then z is said to be the *least upper bound of S*.   In the three preceding examples, the least upper bound of set S is 26, the least upper bound of set T is 3, and the least upper bound of W is 3.   It should be noted that the least upper bound of a given set may or may not be a member of the set.

A set of numbers need not have an upper bound.   For example, consider the set of positive integers, the set of rational numbers, the set of real numbers, or the set of even integers; none of these sets has an upper bound.   However, if a set of *real numbers* does have an upper bound, then the set has a least upper bound.   This is called the completeness property, and we now prove that this is a property of the real numbers.

THEOREM 4.19 *Completeness property.*   Every non-empty set of real numbers with an upper bound has a least upper bound.

Proof: Let A be the set of real numbers defined in the following way: α is in A if and only if there exists a λ in S such that $\lambda > \alpha$.   We first prove that A has the Dedekind properties.

1.   Since S is not empty, there is a λ in S.   Then every $\alpha < \lambda$ is in A. Since S is bounded above, there is a real number β such that $\alpha < \beta$ for every β in S.   Hence, β is not in set A.

2.   If α is in A, then $\alpha < \lambda$ for some λ in S.   If $\beta < \alpha$, then $\beta < \lambda$; thus, β is in A.

Hence, A defines a unique real number θ with the following properties:

$$\alpha < \theta \quad \text{implies } \alpha \text{ is in } A$$

and

$$\beta > \theta \quad \text{implies } \beta \text{ is not in } A.$$

We now prove that θ is the least upper bound of the set S.

I.   Suppose there is a λ in S such that $\lambda > \theta$.   Let α be a real number such that $\theta < \alpha < \lambda$.   Since $\alpha < \lambda$, we conclude that α is in A by definition of set S; but, $\alpha > \theta$ implies that α is not in A.   Since a contradiction results by assuming that there is a λ in S such that $\lambda > \theta$, we conclude that $\lambda \leq \theta$ for all λ in S.   Consequently, θ is an upper bound of the set S.

II.   For every $\varepsilon > 0$, $\theta - \varepsilon < \theta$.   This implies that $\theta - \varepsilon$ is in A; thus, $\theta - \varepsilon < \lambda$ for some λ in S.   Consequently, θ is the least upper bound of S.

Let us now prove that the ordered field of rational numbers does not have the completeness property. This is done by exhibiting a set of rational numbers with an upper bound that does not have a rational number as a least upper bound.

Let S be the set of positive rational numbers x such that $x^2 < 2$. This set is not empty since, for example, 1 is in S. The set has an upper bound; for example, 3 is an upper bound of S. We now prove the assumption that S has an upper bound of S. We now prove that the assumption that S has a rational number as a least upper bound leads to a contradiction.

Suppose z is the rational least upper bound of S. If z is in S, then by definition of S we conclude that z is positive and $z^2 < 2$. If

$$z^2 < 2,$$

then $$z^2 + 2 < 4.$$

Thus, $$(z^2 + 2)z < 4z$$

and

$$z < \frac{4z}{z^2 + 2}.$$

If we let $t = 4z/(z^2 + 2)$, then t is a rational number such that $z < t$. Furthermore,

$$2 - t^2 = 2 - \frac{16z^2}{(z^2 + 2)^2}$$

$$= \frac{2(z^2 + 2)^2 - 16z^2}{(z^2 + 2)^2}$$

$$= \frac{2}{(z^2 + 2)^2} (z^4 + 4z^2 + 4 - 8z^2)$$

$$= \frac{2(z^2 - 2)^2}{(z^2 + 2)^2}.$$

Now, since $\dfrac{2(z^2 - 2)^2}{(z^2 + 2)^2}$ is positive, $2 - t^2 > 0$. Hence, $t^2 < 2$ and we conclude that t is in S. Furthermore, since t is *greater* than z, this contradicts the assumption that the least upper bound z is in S. If z is not in S, then z is a positive rational number such that $z^2 = 2$ or $z^2 > 2$. Since no rational number has 2 as its square, the only remaining possibility for the rational least upper bound z is that $z^2 > 2$.

If $$z^2 > 2,$$

then $$2z^2 > 2 + z^2$$

by adding z^2 to both sides. Hence,

$$z > \frac{2 + z^2}{2z}$$

by dividing by the positive number $2z$.

If we let $u = \dfrac{2 + z^2}{2z}$, then u is a positive rational number and $u < z$. Now, if we can show that $u^2 > 2$, then u would be an upper bound of S less than the (assumed) least upper bound z;

$$u^2 - 2 = \frac{(2 + z^2)^2}{4z^2} - 2$$

$$= \frac{4 + 4z^2 + z^4 - 8z^2}{4z^2}$$

$$= \frac{(2 - z^2)^2}{4z^2}, \quad \text{a positive number.}$$

Thus, $u^2 - 2 > 0$ and $u^2 > 2$. We have proved that if the set S had a rational number z as a least upper bound then the rational number z^2 is not less than 2, equal to 2, or greater than 2; this contradicts the trichotomy property for the rational numbers. Hence, the set S has no rational number as a least upper bound.

The set T of positive *real numbers* whose squares are less than 2 has an upper bound and by the completeness property has a least upper bound. In fact, the least upper bound is the irrational real number $\sqrt{2}$.

EXERCISES

1. Prove that there is no rational number whose square is 3. (You may use the fact that if p is a prime factor of the product of ab where a and b are integers, then p is a factor of a or p is a factor of b.)

2. If T is the set of positive rational numbers x such that $x^2 < 3$, prove that T does not have a rational number as a least upper bound.   Hint: Assume z is the rational least upper bound and let $t = \dfrac{6z}{z^2 + 3}$ and $u = \dfrac{z^2 + 3}{2z}$.

3. Prove there is no rational number x such that $x^3 = 7$.

5 THE COMPLEX NUMBERS

5.1 Introduction

Let us turn our attention to an important mathematical problem that required hundreds of years to solve completely; mathematicians sought to derive formulas that would give the roots of polynomial equations of different degrees.   For the linear equation $ax + b = 0$, where $a \neq 0$, a real (number) solution r_1 always exists and it is $r_1 = -b/a$.   The Hindu and Arabian mathematicians developed the quadratic formula.   They found that the quadratic equation $ax^2 + bx + c = 0$, where $a \neq 0$, always has real solutions provided $b^2 - 4ac \geq 0$; they are given by $\dfrac{-b \pm \sqrt{b^2 - 4ac}}{2a}$.   That is, the two solutions are $r_1 = \dfrac{-b + \sqrt{b^2 - 4ac}}{2a}$ and $r_2 = \dfrac{-b - \sqrt{b^2 - 4ac}}{2a}$.   As a consequence of the ordered field properties, no real numbers exist whose square is negative (see Theorem 3.12); "solutions" where $b^2 - 4ac < 0$ were not seriously considered until the sixteenth century.   Up until that time, there had never been any compelling reasons to consider "numbers" such as x where $x^2 = -4$.

In 1515, Scipio del Ferro discovered that the equation $x^3 + px = q$ was satisfied by

$$x = \sqrt[3]{\sqrt{\frac{p^3}{27} + \frac{q^2}{4}} + \frac{q}{2}} - \sqrt[3]{\sqrt{\frac{p^3}{27} + \frac{q^2}{4}} - \frac{q}{2}}$$

Since every cubic equation $ay^3 + by^2 + cy + d = 0$, where $a \neq 0$, can be transformed by the linear substitution $y = x - b/3a$ into a cubic equation of the form $x^3 + px = q$, this solution is quite significant.   Although the solution is not easy to derive, it can be shown to be a solution in a straight-forward manner using only elementary algebra. Let

$$u = \sqrt{\frac{p^3}{27} + \frac{q^2}{4}} \quad \text{and} \quad v = \frac{q}{2}; \quad \text{then} \quad (u^2 - v^2)^{1/3} = \frac{p}{3}.$$

We wish to prove that

$$[(u + v)^{1/3} - (u - v)^{1/3}]^3 + p[(u + v)^{1/3} - (u - v)^{1/3}] = q.$$

The proof follows:

$$[(u + v)^{1/3} - (u - v)^{1/3}]^3 + p[(u + v)^{1/3} - (u - v)^{1/3}]$$

$$= (u + v) - 3(u + v)^{2/3}(u - v) + 3(u + v)^{1/3}(u - v)^{2/3} - (u - v)$$
$$+ p(u + v)^{1/3} - p(u - v)^{1/3}$$

$$= 2v - 3(u + v)^{1/3}(u^2 - v^2)^{1/3} + 3(u^2 - v^2)^{1/3}(u - v)^{1/3} + p(u + v)^{1/3}$$
$$- p(u - v)^{1/3}$$

$$= 2v + (u + v)^{1/3}[p - 3(u^2 - v^2)^{1/3}] + (u - v)^{1/3}[3(u^2 - v^2)^{1/3} - p]$$

$$= 2v + (u + v)^{1/3}[p - p] + (u - v)^{1/3}[p - p] = 2v = q.$$

In 1535, an Italian named Nicoli Fontana, who received the nickname Tartaglia because of a speech stammer, rediscovered the solution of Ferro; he communicated his solution to Girolamo Cardano (1501–1576) who published the result in 1545 in his book on algebra. Although Cardano was not primarily responsible for the discovery of the formula for solving the cubic equation, it is generally referred to as Cardano's formula, or Cardan's formula.

In 1572, Raffael Bombelli studied the cubic equation $x^3 - 15x = 4$. This equation has three real solutions; they are $r_1 = 4$, $r_2 = -2 + \sqrt{3}$, and $r_3 = -2 - \sqrt{3}$, as the reader may check. Using the cubic formula where $p = -15$ and $q = 4$, we obtain the expression

$$x = \sqrt[3]{\sqrt{-121} + 2} - \sqrt[3]{\sqrt{-121} - 2}.$$

Bombelli's example showed that the formula for the cubic equation led to the heretofore meaningless expression $\sqrt{-121}$. Prior to this time when such an expression resulted in solving quadratic equations, it was ignored and considered to have no mathematical meaning and no practical application. However, Bombelli noticed that treating $\sqrt{-121}$ in a formal algebraic manner led to very desirable results. Formally,

$$\sqrt{-121} = \sqrt{(121)(-1)} = \sqrt{121}\sqrt{-1} = 11\sqrt{-1}.$$

Furthermore,

$$(2 + \sqrt{-1})^3 = 2^3 + 3(2)^2(\sqrt{-1}) + 3(2)(\sqrt{-1})^2 + (\sqrt{-1})^3$$
$$= 8 + 12\sqrt{-1} - 6 - \sqrt{-1}$$
$$= 11\sqrt{-1} + 2.$$

Thus, $\sqrt[3]{\sqrt{-121}} + 2 = 2 + \sqrt{-1}$. Similarly, we can "prove" by cubing $(-2 + \sqrt{-1})$ that $\sqrt[3]{\sqrt{-121}} - 2 = -2 + \sqrt{-1}$. Consequently, substituting in the cubic formula,

$$x = (2 + \sqrt{-1}) - (-2 + \sqrt{-1})$$
$$= 2 + \sqrt{-1} + 2 - \sqrt{-1}$$
$$= 4, \quad \text{a } \textit{real root} \text{ of the given equation.}$$

This practical application of obtaining a real solution to a cubic equation by use of what are today called complex numbers was enough to motivate Bombelli to develop a theory of complex numbers and to move them along the road toward mathematical respectability. It was not until the nineteenth century, however, that complex numbers gained full acceptance in the mathematical community.

Before defining the complex numbers, we digress to complete the story of the discovery of formulas to solve polynomial equations. Ferrari, a student of Cardan, discovered that the problem of solving the biquadratic (or quartic) equation $ax^4 + bx^3 + cx^2 + dx + e = 0$ could be reduced to that of solving a cubic equation; this result also was published by Cardan in 1545. Mathematicians searched many years to find a formula to solve not only the general fifth-degree equation but also equations of higher degree; it was proved by the French mathematician Evariste Galois that they were attempting the impossible. The brilliant Galois, who had a profound influence on the development of modern mathematics, proved that *no formula could exist* to solve a general equation of degree more than four. Of course it was necessary to give some precise definition of *formula* before such a result could be proved; essentially, a formula for the solution of an equation means an expression involving only the coefficients of the equation and a finite number of algebraic operations on these numbers. It is difficult to imagine the influence that Galois might have had on mathematics had he not been killed in a duel in 1832 at the age of 21.

5.2 Complex Numbers

It is not necessary to assume that there is a set containing such numbers as $\sqrt{-121}$ having the field properties. We shall define the complex numbers, define addition and multiplication for these numbers, and prove that this set of numbers has the properties of a field.

An ordered pair (a, b) of *real numbers* is a *complex number*; (a, b) is called the *rectangular* notation for complex numbers. Let $z = (a, b)$ and $w = (c, d)$ be two complex numbers. We define z to be *equal* to w, denoted by $z = w$, if and only if $a = c$ and $b = d$.

An ordered pair of real numbers is assumed to represent a unique point in the rectangular cartesian coordinate plane; hence, our definition of equality makes the set of complex numbers in one-to-one correspondence with the points in the coordinate plane. Although this geometric interpretation has nothing to do with the axiomatic development of the complex numbers, it is important in promoting understanding of various properties of complex numbers.

For any pair of complex numbers $z = (a, b)$ and $w = (c, d)$, we define the *sum* and *product* of z and w, denoted by $z + w$ and zw, respectively, by the following.

1. $z + w = (a + c, b + d)$
2. $zw \quad = (ac - bd, ad + bc)$

Before proving that the set of complex numbers has the field properties, let us consider the geometric interpretations of addition and multiplication of complex numbers.

5.3   Complex Plane

The complex number $z = (a, b)$ where a and b are real numbers represents a point in the cartesian coordinate plane; the real number $\sqrt{a^2 + b^2}$ is the distance of this point from the origin of the coordinate system. (See Figure 5.1). The real number $\sqrt{a^2 + b^2}$ is called the *absolute value* of the complex number z, or the *modulus* of z; the absolute value of z is denoted by $|z|$. By definition, $|z|$ is a non-negative real number and $|z| = \sqrt{a^2 + b^2}$.

An oriented line segment from the origin to the point (a, b) associated with a complex number z is often called a *vector*. The origin $(0, 0)$ is called the *initial point* of the vector and the point associated with the complex number (a, b) is called the *terminal point* of the vector. A vector is often denoted by an arrow as in Figure 5.2. The length of the vector is the absolute value of the complex number (a, b). The angle that the vector makes with the positive x-axis is called the *amplitude* of z, or *argument* of z.

If θ is the amplitude of the complex number $z = (a, b)$ and $r = \sqrt{a^2 + b^2}$ is the absolute value, then $a = r \cos \theta$ and $b = r \sin \theta$.

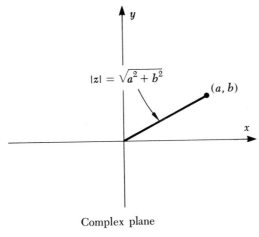

Complex plane

Absolute value

FIGURE 5.1

If $z = (a, b)$ and $w = (c, d)$ are two complex numbers representing points in the complex plane as in Figure 5.3, the sum $(a + c, b + d)$ is the point in the plane which is the vertex opposite the origin in the parallelogram formed with the vectors to z and w as adjacent sides. This should be clear by observing in Figure 5.3 that triangles OPQ and STR are congruent. If (a, b) and (c, d) are two complex numbers with moduli r and t and amplitudes

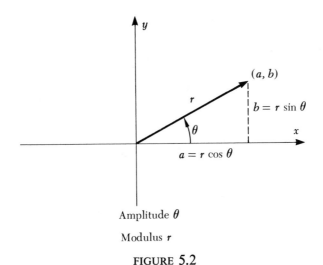

Amplitude θ

Modulus r

FIGURE 5.2

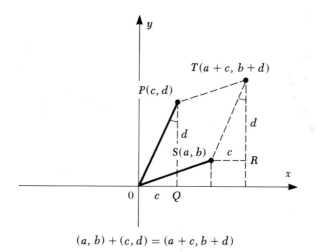

$$(a, b) + (c, d) = (a + c, b + d)$$

FIGURE 5.3

θ and ϕ, respectively, then $(a, b) = (r \cos \theta, r \sin \theta)$ and $(c, d) = (t \cos \phi, t \sin \phi)$. By definition of multiplication,

$$(a, b)(c, d) = (r \cos \theta, r \sin \theta)(t \cos \phi, t \sin \phi)$$
$$= (rt \cos \theta \cos \phi - rt \sin \theta \sin \phi, rt \sin \phi \cos \theta + rt \sin \theta \cos \phi)$$
$$= (rt \cos (\theta + \phi), rt \sin (\theta + \phi)).$$

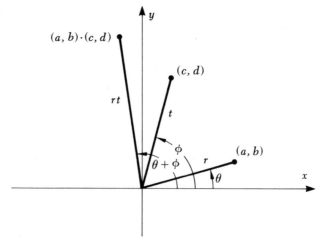

Product of complex numbers

FIGURE 5.4

Thus, the product of (a, b) and (c, d) is that complex number with amplitude $\theta + \phi$ and absolute value rt.   Geometrically, to multiply z and w one adds the amplitude of one complex number to the amplitude of the other; then, the product is the point on the terminal side of this angle at a distance from the origin equal to the product of the distances from the origin (moduli) of the two given complex numbers.   From this interpretation of multiplication, it should be geometrically obvious that $zw = wz$.   Furthermore, since the complex number $(1, 0)$ has $0°$ as amplitude and 1 as modulus, it is geometrically clear that the complex number $(1, 0)$ is the multiplicative identity for the set of complex numbers.

5.4   Field Properties

We now prove that the set of complex numbers has the field properties. The reader should discuss the geometric significance of each property in relation to the coordinate system and give a geometric argument to justify the validity of each property.

THEOREM 5.1   *Commutative property of addition.*   For complex numbers (a, b) and (c, d)

$$(a, b) + (c, d) = (c, d) + (a, b).$$

Proof: $(a, b) + (c, d) = (a + c, b + d)$ DEFINITION OF ADDITION

$= (c + a, d + b)$ COMMUTATIVE PROPERTY OF ADDITION FOR REAL NUMBERS

$= (c, d) + (a, b)$ DEFINITION OF ADDITION

THEOREM   5.2   *Commutative   property   of   multiplication.*   For complex numbers (a, b) and (c, d),

$$(a, b)(c, d) = (c, d)(a, b).$$

Proof: Left as an exercise for the reader.

THEOREM 5.3   *Associative property of addition.*   For complex numbers (a, b), (c, d), and (e, f),

$$[(a, b) + (c, d)] + (e, f) = (a, b) + [(c, d) + (e, f)].$$

Proof:

$$[(a, b) + (c, d)] + (e, f) = (a + c, b + d) + (e, f)$$
$$= ((a + c) + e, (b + d) + f)$$
$$= (a + (c + e), b + (d + f))$$
$$= (a, b) + (c + e, d + f)$$
$$= (a, b) + [(c, d) + (e, f)].$$

THEOREM 5.4   *Associative property of multiplication.*   For complex numbers (a, b), (c, d), and (e, f),

$$\{(a, b)(c, d)\}(e, f) = (a, b)\{(c, d)(e, f)\}.$$

Proof: Left as an exercise for the reader.

THEOREM 5.5   *Existence of additive identity.*   For any complex number (a, b), $(a, b) + (0, 0) = (a, b)$.

Proof: $(a, b) + (0, 0) = (a + 0, b + 0)$
$$= (a, b).$$

THEOREM 5.6   *Existence of additive inverses.*   For the complex number (a, b), $(-a, -b)$ is the additive inverse of (a, b).

Proof: Left as an exercise for the reader.

THEOREM 5.7   *Existence of multiplicative identity.*   For any complex number (a, b), $(a, b)(1, 0) = (a, b)$.

Proof: Left as an exercise for the reader.

THEOREM 5.8   *Existence of multiplicative inverses.*   Each complex number (a, b) different from the additive identity $(0, 0)$ has $(a/(a^2 + b^2), -b/(a^2 + b^2))$ as its multiplicative inverse.

Proof: Left as an exercise for the reader.

THEOREM 5.9   *Distributive property.*   For the complex numbers (a, b), (c, d), and (e, f),

$$(a, b)[(c, d) + (e, f)] = (a, b)(c, d) + (a, b)(e, f).$$

Proof: Left as an exercise for the reader.

5.5   Gaussian Notation

We identify the real number a with the complex number $(a, 0)$. Geometrically, this is equivalent to associating each real number with a point on the x-axis in the complex plane; thus, the x-axis is often called the *real axis*.   This identification makes the set of real numbers isomorphic to a subset of the set of complex numbers; a justification of this fact is left as an exercise for the reader.

The symbol i denotes the complex number $(0, 1)$.   It should be noted that $(b, 0)(0, 1) = (0, b)$ as a consequence of the definition of multiplication for complex numbers.   Hence,

$$(a, b) = (a, 0) + (0, b)$$

$$= (a, 0) + (b, 0)(0, 1).$$

Thus, the notation $a + bi$ is used to denote the complex number (a, b) and is called the Gaussian notation for complex numbers.

If $z = a + bi$, then a is called the real part of z and we write $a = R(z)$; the real number b is called the imaginary part of z and we write $b = I(z)$. It is important to notice that $R(z)$ and $I(z)$ are real numbers.

The Gaussian notation has the advantage that by using the fact that $i^2 = -1$ it is possible to add, multiply, subtract, and divide complex numbers in a formal algebraic fashion.

EXAMPLES

1. $(2 + 3i) + (6 - 8i) = (2 + 6) + (3i - 8i) = 8 - 5i$
2. $(8 + 5i) - (1 - 2i) = 7 + 7i$
3. $(2 + 4i)(2 - 3i) = 4 + 8i - 6i - 12i^2 = 16 + 2i$
4. $\dfrac{3 + 2i}{2 + 5i} = \dfrac{3 + 2i}{2 + 5i} \cdot \dfrac{2 - 5i}{2 - 5i} = \dfrac{6 - 11i - 10i^2}{4 - 25i^2} = \dfrac{16 - 11i}{29}$

$$= \frac{16}{29} - \frac{11}{29} i$$

The complex number $a - bi$ is called the *conjugate* of $a + bi$; if $z = a + bi$ we denote the conjugate of z by $\bar{z} = a - bi$.   Note that the conjugate of the conjugate of z is z; symbolically, $\bar{\bar{z}} = z$.   To find the quotient of two complex numbers $\dfrac{c + di}{a + bi}$, we multiply the numerator and denominator by the conjugate $a - bi$ of the denominator as in Example 4 above.   The following theorem proves some of the important properties of complex numbers concerning absolute value and conjugate.

THEOREM 5.10   Let $z = a + bi$ and $w = c + di$ be complex numbers. Then,

(a) $z \cdot \bar{z} = |z|^2 = [R(z)]^2 + [I(z)]^2$
(b) $|z| \geq R(z)$
(c) $\overline{zw} = \bar{z} \cdot \bar{w}$
(d) $|zw| = |z| |w|$
(e) $|zw| \geq R(z \cdot \bar{w})$
(f) $\overline{z + w} = \bar{z} + \bar{w}$
(g) $z + \bar{z} = 2R(z)$.

Proof:

(a) $z \cdot \bar{z} = (a + bi)(a - bi)$

$\qquad = a^2 + b^2 = |z|^2$

$\qquad = [R(z)]^2 + [I(z)]^2.$

(b) Since $|z|^2 = [R(z)]^2 + [I(z)]^2$ and since $|z|$, $[R(z)]^2$, and $[I(z)]^2$ are non-negative real numbers,

$$|z|^2 \geq [R(z)]^2$$

and $\qquad\qquad\qquad\qquad |z| \geq R(z).$

(c) $\overline{zw} = \overline{(a + bi)(c + di)}$

$\qquad = \overline{(ac - bd) + (ad + bc)i}$

$\qquad = (ac - bd) - (ad + bc)i$

$\qquad = (a - bi)(c - di)$

$\qquad = \bar{z} \cdot \bar{w}.$

(d) $|zw|^2 = (zw)(\overline{z \cdot w})$ $\qquad$ by part a.

$\qquad = (zw)(\bar{z} \cdot \bar{w})$ $\qquad$ by part c.

$\qquad = (z \cdot \bar{z})(w \cdot \bar{w})$ $\qquad$ by the field properties.

$\qquad = |z|^2 |w|^2$ $\qquad$ by part a.

Since $|zw|$, $|z|$, and $|w|$ are non-negative real numbers, we may take square roots of both sides of the equation

$$|zw|^2 = |z|^2 |w|^2$$

and obtain $\qquad\qquad\qquad\qquad |zw| = |z| |w|.$

In other words, the absolute value of a product of two complex numbers is the product of the absolute values.

(e) $\quad |zw| = |z|\,|w| \qquad$ by part d.

$\qquad = |z|\,|\bar{w}| \qquad$ since $|w| = |\bar{w}|$.

$\qquad = |z\cdot\bar{w}| \qquad$ by part d.

$\qquad \geq R(z\cdot\bar{w}) \qquad$ by part b.

(f) $\quad \overline{z + w} = \overline{(a + bi) + (c + di)}$

$\qquad = \overline{(a + c) + (b + d)i}$

$\qquad = (a + c) - (b + d)i$

$\qquad = (a - bi) + (c - di)$

$\qquad = \bar{z} + \bar{w}.$

In other words, the conjugate of the sum of two complex numbers is the sum of the conjugates of each of the complex numbers.

(g) $\quad z + \bar{z} = (a + bi) + (a - bi)$

$\qquad = 2a$

$\qquad = 2R(z).$

We use this theorem to prove the important triangular inequality for complex numbers. We wish to prove that if $|z + w| \leq |z| + |w|$, the absolute value of the sum of two complex numbers is less than or equal to the sum of the absolute values.

$|z + w|^2 = (z + w)\overline{(z + w)} \qquad$ by part a.

$\qquad = (z + w)(\bar{z} + \bar{w}) \qquad$ by part f.

$\qquad = z\cdot\bar{z} + w\cdot\bar{w} + z\cdot\bar{w} + \bar{z}\cdot w \qquad$ by the field properties.

$\qquad = |z|^2 + |w|^2 + z\cdot\bar{w} + \bar{z}\cdot w \qquad$ by part a.

$\qquad = |z|^2 + |w|^2 + z\cdot\bar{w} + \overline{z\cdot w} \qquad$ by part c.

$\qquad = |z|^2 + |w|^2 + 2R(z\cdot\bar{w}) \qquad$ by part g.

$\qquad \leq |z|^2 + |w|^2 + 2|z\cdot w| \qquad$ by part e.

$\qquad \leq |z|^2 + 2|z|\,|w| + |w|^2 \qquad$ by part d.

$\qquad \leq (|z| + |w|)^2 \qquad$ by the field properties.

Since $|z + w|$ and $|z| + |w|$ are non-negative real numbers, we conclude

$$|z + w| \leq |z| + |w|.$$

Since $|z|$ and $|w|$ are the distances of z and w from the origin and since $|z + w|$ is the distance of $z + w$ from the origin, the theorem is geometrically equivalent to stating that the length of one side of a triangle is less than or equal to the sum of the lengths of the other two sides.

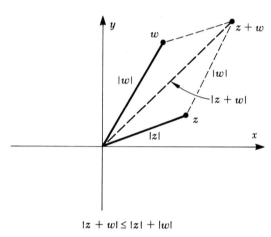

$$|z + w| \leq |z| + |w|$$

Triangular inequality

FIGURE 5.5

It is not difficult to prove that if z is a complex root of the cubic equation $ax^3 + bx^2 + cx + d = 0$, where $a, b, c,$ and d are real numbers, then the conjugate z is also a root of the equation. In general, it can be proved that if z is a complex root of any polynomial equation with real coefficients, then the conjugate z is also a root of the equation. We leave this as an exercise for the reader.

Since we have proved that the square of any element in an ordered field is non-negative, and since there exists a complex number whose square is negative, namely $i^2 = -1$, we have shown that although the set of complex numbers has the field properties it does not have the ordered field properties.

EXERCISES

1. Prove Theorem 5.2.
2. Prove Theorem 5.4.
3. Prove Theorem 5.6.

4. Prove Theorem 5.7.
5. Prove Theorem 5.8.
6. Prove Theorem 5.9.
7. Show that the set of real numbers and the set of complex numbers of the form $(a, 0)$ are isomorphic.
8. Let z be the complex number $\cos \theta + i \sin \theta$. Prove for every positive integer n that $z^n = \cos n\theta + i \sin n\theta$.

ANSWERS
(Odd-Numbered Exercises)

(The author wishes to acknowledge with gratitude the assistance given by Mr. Peter W. Day in the preparation of the answers to the exercises.)

EXERCISES 1.3, page 7

1. Induction: *Part* 1. $1' \neq 1$ by postulate 4. *Part* 2. Assume $k' \neq k$. Then, $(k')' \neq k'$ by the contrapositive of postulate 3.

3. Now, 1 is in S. Suppose k is in S. Then k is a natural number and k' is in S for the choice $m = k$. Thus S contains all natural numbers.

5. $n = 1$ or $n \neq 1$. For given m, if $n = 1$, $m + 1 = m' \neq 1$ by postulate 4. If $n \neq 1$, by Exercise 4 there is a unique natural number q such that $q' = n$. Then $m + n = m + q' = (m + q)' \neq 1$ by postulate 4.

EXERCISES 1.4, page 9

1. $m' \cdot n' + 1 = (m + 1)(n + 1) + 1 = (m + 1)n + (m + 1) \cdot 1 + 1$

$$= mn + n + m + 1 + 1 = mn + (n + 1) + (m + 1)$$

$$= mn + n' + m' = (m' + n') + mn.$$

3. $2n = n \cdot 2 = n \cdot 1' = (n \cdot 1) + n = n + n.$

5. *Part* I. For a particular natural number n let S be the set of all natural numbers m such that at least one natural number can be assigned to $m \cdot n$ satisfying (a) and (b).

I. *Let* $1 \cdot n = n$. (A) $1 \cdot n = n$ implies $1 \cdot 1 = 1$ for $n = 1$, and thus for $m \cdot 1 = m$ when $m = 1$ we have $1 \cdot 1 = 1$. Thus (a) is satisfied by the assignment $1 \cdot n = n$. (B) Letting $1 \cdot n = n$, $1 \cdot n' = n'$. Thus for $m = 1$, $1 \cdot n' = n' = n + 1 = (1 \cdot n) + 1$. Thus (b) is satisfied for this assignment for $m = 1$.

II. Suppose k is in S, i.e., at least one natural number can be assigned to $k \cdot n$ satisfying $k \cdot 1 = k$ and $k \cdot n' = n \cdot n + k$. Let $k' \cdot n = k \cdot n + n$. This assigns a natural number to $k' \cdot n$ since we assume at least one natural number is assigned to $k \cdot n$ and every natural number has a successor. (A) for $n = 1$, since we let $k' \cdot n = k \cdot n + n$, $k' \cdot 1 = k \cdot 1 + 1 = k + 1 = k'$; $k \cdot 1 = k$ since k is in S. Thus, k' satisfies (a). (B) Letting $k' \cdot n = k \cdot n + n$, $k' \cdot n' = k \cdot n' + n' = (k \cdot n + k) + n + 1 = k \cdot n + n + (n + 1) = k' \cdot n + k'$. Thus k' satisfies (b), and since it also satisfies (a), k' is in S. By postulate 5 S contains all natural numbers, and there is at least one natural number that can be assigned to $m \cdot n$ for all m and n which satisfy (a) and (b).

Part II. Suppose more than one natural number, say r and t, $r \neq t$, can be assigned to $m \cdot n$ for some m and n satisfying (a) and (b). Then $m \cdot n = r$, and $m \cdot n = t$. Let S be the set of all natural numbers n such that $r = t$ for a given m. 1 is in S since $r = m \cdot 1 = m$ and $t = m \cdot 1 = m$ and thus $r = t$. Suppose k is in S. Then for $m \cdot k = r$ and $m \cdot k = t$, $r = t$. Now if $m \cdot k' = u$ and $m \cdot k' = v$,

64

$u = m \cdot k + m = r + m$ and $v = m \cdot k + m = r + m$. Since $m \cdot k$ is unique by the induction hypothesis, $u = v$, and k' is in S. Thus S contains all natural numbers.

7. Let S be the set of all natural numbers p such that $m(np) = (mn)p$. For $p = 1$, $m(n \cdot 1) = mn$, and $(mn) \cdot 1 = mn$, so 1 is in S. Suppose k is in S. Then $m(nk) = (mn)k$. Then $m(n \cdot k') = m(nk) + mn = mn(k) + mn = (mn)k + mn$ and $m(nk') = (mn) \cdot k'$. Thus k' is in S and S contains all natural numbers.

EXERCISES 1.6, page 12

1. Let S be the set of all natural numbers n such that $n \geq 1$. Since $1 \geq 1$, 1 is in S. Suppose k is in S. Then $k \geq 1$. Since $k' = k + 1$, $k' > k$ by definition with $q = 1$. If $k = 1$, $k' > 1$. If $k > 1$, $k' > 1$ by transitive property of inequality. Thus k' is in S and S contains all natural numbers.

3. If $m < n$ and $p < q$, there are natural numbers r and s such that $m + r = n$ and $p + s = q$. Then $m + r + p + s = n + q$ and $m + p + (r + s) = n + q$. Since $r + s$ is a natural number, $m + p < n + q$.

5. If $p \neq 1$ there is a unique natural number q such that $q' = p$. Then $m = q' \cdot n = n \cdot q' = nq + n$. Since nq is a natural number, $n < m$.

7. If $m > n$, there exists a natural number q such that $m = n + q$. By problem 1, $q = 1$ or $q > 1$. If $q = 1$, $m = n + 1$. If $q > 1$, $m = n + q > n + 1$. Thus $m \geq n + 1$.

9. I. $m = n$, $p < q$. Then $p + m < q + m$, $m + p < n + q$. Also, $pm < qm$, $mp < nq$, substituting n for m.

    II. If $m < n$, $p < q$. Then $mp < np$ and $pn < qn$, so $np < nq$, and by transitive property, $mp < nq$. Also, $m + p < n + p$ and $p + n < q + n$, $n + p < n + q$, and by transitive property, $m + p < n + q$.

EXERCISES 1.8, page 16

1. (a) I. Since $xy = yx$, $(x, y) \simeq (x, y)$. Thus $\simeq$ is reflexive.

    II. If $(x, y) \simeq (u, v)$, $xv = yu$, $uy = vx$, and thus $(u, v) \simeq (x, y)$. Thus $\simeq$ is symmetric.

    III. If $(x, y) \simeq (u, v)$ and $(u, v) \simeq (w, z)$, then $xv = yu$ and $uz = vw$; Thus, $xvuz = yuvw$ and by the cancellation property of multiplication, $xz = yw$, and we have $(x, y) \simeq (w, z)$. Thus $\simeq$ is transitive. Since $\simeq$ is reflexive, symmetric, and transitive, $\simeq$ is an equivalence relation.

(b) $(2, 3)$, $(4, 6)$, $(8, 12)$, $(16, 24)$, $(32, 48)$, $(64, 96)$.

3. *Part 1.* Assume vRw; thus, wRv by the symmetric property. If x is in v^R, then vRx. By transitive property, wRx, so x is in w^R. Thus, $v^R \subseteq w^R$. If y is in w^R, then wRy. From the assumption vRw and the transitive property for an equivalence relation, we conclude vRy and y is in v^R. Thus, $w^R \subseteq v^R$ and $w^R = v^R$.

Part 2. If $v^R = w^R$, then for any element x in v^R we have x is in w^R. Hence, vRx and wRx. By the symmetric property xRw, and vRw by the transitive property.

5. (a) Yes. (b) No. (c) Yes.

EXERCISES 2.2, page 21

1. If $(a, b)^\sim$ and $(c, d)^\sim$ are positive integers, $a > b$, and $c > d$. Then there is a natural p such that $c = d + p$. Then $ac = ad + ap$ and $bc = bd + bp$. Since $a > b$, $ap > bp$, and $ap + ad + bd > bp + ad + bd$, $(ap + ad) + bd > (bp + bd) + ad$ so $ac + bd > bc + ad$ or $ac + bd > ad + bc$. Since $(a, b)^\sim \cdot (c, d)^\sim = (ac + bd, ad + bc)^\sim$, the product is positive.

3. Let $(a, b)^\sim$ and $(c, d)^\sim$ be any two negative integers. Then $a < b$ and $c < d$, so $a + c < b + d$, and thus $(a, b)^\sim + (c, d)^\sim = (a + c, b + d)^\sim$ is negative.

5. Let $(a, b)^\sim$ be some positive integer and $(c, d)^\sim$ be some negative integer. Then $a > b$ and $c < d$. Then there is a natural number p such that $c + p = d$. Then $ac + ap = ad$ and $bc + bp = bd$. Since $b < a$, $bp < ap$. Then $bp + ac + bc < ap + ac + bc$, $(bp + bc) + ac < (ap + ac) + bc$, $bd + ac < ad + bc$, or $ac + bd < ad + bc$. Since $(a, b)^\sim (c, d)^\sim = (ac + bd, ad + bc)^\sim$ the product is negative.

7. Since $(a + 1) - 1 = a$, $(b + 1) - 1 = b$, and $(c + 1) - 1 = c$, $(a + 1, 1)^\sim = +a$, $(b + 1, 1)^\sim = +b$, and $(c + 1, 1)^\sim = +c$.

$$(+a)(+b) = (a + 1, 1)^\sim (b + 1, 1)^\sim = ((a + 1)(b + 1) + 1, a + 1 + b + 1)^\sim$$
$$= (ab + a + b + 1 + 1, a + b + 1 + 1)^\sim = (ab + 1, 1)^\sim$$
$$= (c + 1, 1)^\sim = +c, \text{ since } ab = c.$$

9. $[(a, b)^\sim (c, d)^\sim](a, f)^\sim = (ac + bd, ad + bc)^\sim (e, f)^\sim$
$$= (ace + bde + adf + bcf, acf + bdf + ade + bce)^\sim$$

$(a, b)^\sim [(c, d)^\sim (e, f)^\sim] = (a, b)^\sim (ce + df, cf + de)^\sim$
$$= (ace + adf + bcf + bde, acf + ade + bcf + bde)^\sim.$$

A comparison of the two shows they are equal.

11. Let x, y, z be integers and suppose $x + z = y + z$. Now there is an integer t such that $z + t = 0$. Then $(x + z) + t = (y + z) + t$, $x + (z + t) = y + (z + t)$, $x + 0 = y + 0$, $x = y$.

EXERCISES 2.3, page 25

1. $x = (a, b)$ has the unique additive inverse $y = (b, a)$. If x is negative, $b > a$, so y is positive. If y is positive, $a < b$, so x is negative. I. Let x be negative. Then $x + y = 0$ and y is positive, so $x < 0$. II. Let $x < 0$. Then there is a positive integer t such that $x + t = 0$. t must be the additive inverse, and since t is positive, x is negative.

3. If $xz < yz$, and $z < 0$, there is a positive integer t such that $z + t = 0$. Then $xz + xt = x \cdot 0 = 0$, and $yz + yt = y \cdot 0 = 0$. Then $xz + xt + yt < yz + xt + yt$, $(xz + zt) + yt < (yz + yt) + xt$, $0 + yt < 0 + xt$, $yt < xt$. Since t is positive, $t > 0$, so $y < x$ or $x > y$.

EXERCISES 3.1, page 30

1. Let 1 and 1* be two multiplicative identities. Then, $(1)(1^*) = 1^*$ and $(1^*)(1) = 1$. Since $(1^*)(1) = (1)(1^*)$, $1^* = 1$.

3. Let t and u be two multiplicative inverses of $x \neq 0$. Then $xt = 1$ and $xu = 1$. Thus $xt = xu$, and by Theorem 3.4, since $x \neq 0$, $t = u$.

5. If $xy = 0$ and $x \neq 0$, $xy = yx = 0 \cdot x$ and by Theorem 3.4, $y = 0$. If $y \neq 0$, $xy = 0 \cdot y$ and by Theorem 3.4, $x = 0$. Thus either $x = 0$ or $y = 0$.

7. Since $1 \neq 0$ by property 9, we have by Theorem 3.12 that $1^2 = (1)(1) = 1 > 0$.

9. $-(-x) + (-x) = 0$ so $[-(-x) + -x] + x = 0 + x = x$, $-(-x) + (-x + x) = x$, $-(-x) + 0 = x$, $-(-x) = x$.

EXERCISES 3.2, page 31

1. $[(a, b)^* + (c, d)^*] + (e, f)^* = (ad + bc, bd)^* + (e, f)^*$
$$= (adf + bcf + bde, bdf)^* \text{ and}$$
$(a, b)^* + [(c, d)^* + (e, f)^*] = (a, b)^* + (cf + de, df)^*$
$$= (adf + bcf + bde, bdf)^*$$
and they are the same.

3. $(a, b)^* + (-a, b)^* = (ab + (-a)b, b^2)^* = (-ab + ab, b^2)^* = (0, b^2)^*$, since $b \neq 0$, $(0, b^2)^*$ is a rational; since $(0)(1) = (b^2)(0)$, $(0, b^2)^* = (0, 1)^*$ and the theorem is proved.

EXERCISES 3.4, page 35

1. $[(a, b)^*(c, d)^*](e, f)^* = (ac, bd)^*(e, f)^* = (ace, bdf)^*$
$(a, b)^*[(c, d)^*(e, f)^*] = (a, b)^*(ce, df)^* = (ace, bdf)^*$
and the two are equal.

3. $(a, b)^*(b, a)^* = (ab, ab)^*$. Since $a \neq 0$ and $b \neq 0$, $ab \neq 0$ and $(ab, ab)^*$ is a rational number. Since $(ab)1 = 1(ab)$, $(ab, ab)^* = (1, 1)^*$, and the theorem is proved.

5. If $(a, b)^*$ and $(c, d)^*$ are positive rationals, we may assume without loss of generality that $ab > 0$ and $cd > 0$, and $a, b, c, d > 0$. Then $ad + bc > 0$ and $bd > 0$, so $(ad + bc)bd > 0$, and thus $(a, b)^* + (c, d)^* = (ad + bc, bd)^*$ is positive.

7. Let $(a, 1)^* = a$, $(b, 1)^* = b$, $(c, 1)^* = c$. I. If $ab = c$, $(a)(b) = (a, 1)^* \cdot (b, 1)^* = (ab, 1)^* = (c, 1)^* = c$. II. If $a + b = c$, $a + b = (a, 1)^* + (b, 1)^* = (a + b, 1)^* = (c, 1)^* = c$.

9. (a) Let $s = (a, b)^* > 0$. Then $ab > 0$ and $a \neq 0$. Now take $p = (b + a, a)^*$, a rational number since $a \neq 0$. Then $ps = (b + a, a)^* \cdot (a, b)^* = (ab + a^2, ab)^*$, so $ps = 1 + s$ for this choice of p. Since $s > 0$, $ps > 1$.

(b) If $s = (a, b)^*$ and $t = (c, d)^* > 0$, take $r = (ad + bc, bc)^*$. $c \neq 0$, and $b \neq 0$, so $bc \neq 0$ and r is a rational. Then,

$$rt = (ad + bc, bc)^*(c, d)^* = (acd + bc^2, bcd)^* = (c^2, cd)^* + (a, b)^*$$

$$= (c, c)^*(c, d)^* + (a, b)^* = (c, d)^* + (a, b)^* = t + s.$$

Since $t > 0$ is given, $rt > s$.

EXERCISES 4.2, page 38

1. Yes. 0 is in γ and 3 is not in γ. Suppose x is in γ. If $x \leq 0$ and $t < x$, $t < 0$, so t is in γ. If $x > 0$ and $t < x$, $t^2 < x^2$ and $x^2 < 2$, so $t^2 < 2$ and t is in γ. Again suppose x is in γ. If $x \leq 0$, take $t = 1$. Then $t > x$, and t is in γ. If $x > 0$, take $t = (4x)/(x^2 + 2)$. Since x is in γ, $x^2 < 2$, $x^2 + 2 < 4$, $x(x^2 + 2) < 4x$, and $x < (4x)/(x^2 + 2) = t$. Also since $x^2 < 2$, $x^2 - 2 < 0$, $(x^2 - 2)^2 > 0$, $x^4 - 4x^2 + 4 > 0$, $x^4 + 4x^2 + 4 > 8x^2$, $2(x^2 + 2)^2 > 16x^2$, $2 > [(4x)/(x^2 + 2)]^2 = t^2$, so for this t, $t > x$ and t is in γ.

3. -1 is in λ, and 4 is not in λ. If x is in λ, and $t < x$, $t^3 < x^3 < 5$, so t is in λ. Suppose s is in λ. If $s \leq 0$, for $t = 1$, $t > s$ and t is in λ. If $s > 0$, take $t = (15s)/(s^3 + 10)$. Since s is in λ, $s^3 < 5$, $s^3 + 10 < 15$, $s(s^3 + 10) < 15s$, $s < (15s)/(s^3 + 10) = t$. Also since $s^3 < 5$, $(s^3 - 5)^2 > 0$, so $(s^3 - 5)^2(s^3 + 40) > 0$, $s^9 + 30s^6 - 375s^3 + 1000 > 0$, $s^9 + 30s^6 + 300s^3 + 1000 > 675s^3$, $5(s^3 + 10)^3 > 3375s^3$, $5 > [(15s)/(s^3 + 10)]^3 = t^3$. Thus, for this t, $t > s$ and t is in λ.

5. $a - 1 < a$ and $a + 1 > a$, so $a - 1$ is in α and $a + 1$ is not in α. If s is in α and $t < s$, $s < a$ and thus $t < a$, so t is in α. If s is in α, for $t = (s + a)/2$, $s < t < a$, so t is in α.

7. Suppose $s > t$ for every t in α and s is in α. Then there is a rational p in α such that $p > s$. Contradiction. Thus s is not in α.

9. For p in α, since $s > 0$, $p - s$ is in α, so for $x < p - s$, x is in α, and since $x + s < p$, $x + s$ is in α. Thus for $t_n = x + ns$, there is an $N > 0$ for which t_N is in α (namely $N = 1$ here). Since $s > 0$, for any rational $v > x$, there is an $N > 0$ such that $t_N > v$, namely any $N > (v - x)/s$. Since there is a rational u in $C(\alpha)$, there is an $M > 0$ such that $t_M > u$, and thus for some $N > 0$, t_N is in α and t_{N+1} is in $C(\alpha)$. If t_{N+1} is not the least element of $C(\alpha)$, take $q = t_{N+1}$ and $p = t_N$. Then $q + (-p) = x + s(N + 1) - x - sN = s$. If $t_{N+1} = x + s(N + 1)$ is the least element, since $s > 0$, $s/2 < s$, $x + sN + s/2 < x + sN + s = t_{N+1}$, so $x + sN + s/2$ is in α. Let $y = x + s/2$, and $r_n = y + sn$. Then

$r_N = x + s/2 + sN$ is in α and $r_{N+1} = x + s/2 + sN > t_{n+1}$, so r_{N+1} is in $C(\alpha)$, and r_{N+1} is not the least element of $C(\alpha)$. Thus, take $p = r_N$, $q = r_{N+1}$. Then $q + (-p) = y + sN + s - y - sM = s$.

EXERCISES 4.3, page 42

1. Let $\bar{c} = \{x$ such that $x < (a + b)/2\}$. If $a \geq b$, $\bar{a} \geq \bar{b}$. Since $\bar{a} < \bar{b}$, $a < b$. If t is in $\bar{a}$, $t < a < (a + b)/2$, so t is in $\bar{c}$. If t is in $\bar{c}$, $t < (a + b)/2 < b$, so t is in $\bar{b}$. Since $b > a$, $3a + b > 4a$, $(3a + b)/4 > a$. Also, since $a < b$, $3a + b < 2a + 2b$, $(3a + b)/4 < (a + b)/2$, so for $t = (3a + b)/4$, t is in $\bar{c}$ but not in $\bar{a}$. Thus, $\bar{a} < \bar{c}$. Since $a < b$, $a + 3b < 4b$, $(a + 3b)/4 < b$. Also, since $b > a$, $3b + a > 2a$, $(3b + a)/4 > (a + b)/2$. Thus for $s = (3b + a)/4$, s is in b but s is not in $\bar{c}$. Thus $\bar{c} < \bar{b}$, and since $a < c$, $a < c < b$.

3. If α is positive, $\alpha > \bar{0}$. Thus there is a rational p in α such that p is not in $\bar{0}$. Thus $p \geq 0$. Since p is in α and α is real, there is another rational $s > p$ such that s is in α. Then $s > 0$, and s is in α.

5. If y is in β but y is not in α, then $y > x$ for every x in α. Thus if t is in α, $t < y$, and since y is in β, t is in β. Thus $\alpha \subseteq \beta$; but since y is in β and not in α, $\alpha \subset \beta$, so $\alpha < \beta$.

7. If $\alpha < \bar{0}$, there is a rational p in $\bar{0}$ such that p is not in α. Then there is a $q > p$ for which q is in $\bar{0}$. Since p is not in α, p is in $C(\alpha)$, so q is in $C'(\alpha)$. Since q is in $\bar{0}$, $q < 0$, so $-q > 0$, and thus $-q$ is in $(-\alpha)$ and $-q$ is not in $\bar{0}$. By problem 5 $(-\alpha) > \bar{0}$.

EXERCISES 4.4, page 45

1. For rational x, $\bar{2} = \{x$ such that $x < 2\}$, $\bar{3} = \{x$ such that $x < 3\}$, $\bar{6} = \{x$ such that $x < 6\}$, $\bar{2} \cdot \bar{3} = \{x$ such that $x \leq 0$, or $x = pq, p, q > 0, p$ in $\bar{2}$, q in $\bar{3}\}$. I. Let t be in $\bar{2} \cdot \bar{3}$. If $t \leq 0$, t is in $\bar{6}$. If $t > 0$, $t = pq, p < 2, q < 3$, so $t = pq < 6$, and t is in $\bar{6}$. Thus $\bar{2} \cdot \bar{3} \subseteq \bar{6}$. II. Let t be in $\bar{6}$. If $t \leq 0$, t is in $\bar{2} \cdot \bar{3}$. If $t > 0$, $t < 6$, so $t/3 < 2$ and thus $t/3$ is in $\bar{2}$, so there is a q such that $0 < t/3 < q < 2$. Then $t/q < 3$, so t/q is in $\bar{3}$. Then for $p = t/q > 0$, $pq = (t/q)q = t$, so t is in $\bar{2} \cdot \bar{3}$. Thus $\bar{6} \subseteq \bar{2} \cdot \bar{3}$. By definition of set equality, $\bar{2} \cdot \bar{3} = \bar{6}$.

EXERCISES 4.5, page 47

1. We need only to prove theorem 4.15 for $\gamma > 0$ and not both α and $\beta > 0$. Let $\alpha < \beta$. I. If $\alpha < 0$, and $\beta > 0$, since $\gamma > 0$, $\alpha\gamma = -[(-\alpha)\gamma] < 0$, and $\beta\gamma > 0$, so $\alpha\gamma < \beta\gamma$. II. Now we cannot have $\alpha > 0$, $\beta < 0$, and $\alpha < \beta$; the only case remaining is when $\alpha < 0$, and $\beta < 0$. Since $\gamma > 0$, $\alpha\gamma = -[(-\alpha)\gamma]$ and $\beta\gamma = -[(-\beta)\gamma]$. If $\alpha < \beta$, $\alpha + (-\alpha) + (-\beta) < \beta + (-\beta) + (-\alpha)$ and $-\alpha > -\beta$. Thus, $(-\alpha)\gamma > (-\beta)\gamma$ and $-[(-\alpha)\gamma] < -[(-\beta)\gamma]$, so $\alpha\gamma < \beta\gamma$.

EXERCISES 4.6, page 50

1. Proof by contradiction. Assume there is a rational number x such that $x^2 = 3$. Then $x = a/b$ for some integers a and b which have no factor in common other than 1. Then $x^2 = a^2/b^2 = 3$, $a^2 = 3b^2$, and 3 divides a^2. Now, if 3 does not divide an integer a, a is of the form $a = 3n + 1$ or $a = 3n + 2$ for some integer n, in which case $a^2 = 9n^2 + 6n + 1 = 3(3n^2 + 2n) + 1$ or $a^2 + 9n^2 + 12n + 4 = 3(3n^2 + 4n + 1) + 1$, so 3 does not divide a^2. Thus, by the contrapositive of the above, if 3 divides a^2, 3 divides a. In this case, for some integer t, $a = 3t$, and $a^2 = (3t)^2 = 9t^2 = 3b^2$ so $b^2 = 3t^2$ and 3 divides b^2, so 3 divides b. Thus, 3 divides both a and b, and they have the factor 3 in common. Contradiction.

3. Proof by contradiction. Assume there is a rational x such that $x^3 = 7$. Then $x = a/b$ for some integers a and b which have no common factor other than 1. Then $x^3 = a^3/b^3 = 7$, $a^3 = 7b^3$, so 7 divides a^3. Now, if 7 does not divide an integer a, then a can be written in the form $a = 7n + s$ for some integer n and for some integer s where $1 \le s \le 6$. Then $a^3 = 343n^3 + 147n^2s + 21ns^2 + s^3 = 7A + s^3$ where $A = 49n^3 + 21n^2s + 3ns^2$ and $s^3 = 1, 8, 27, 64, 125,$ or 216. Then $a^3 = 7A + 1$, $7(A + 1) + 1$, $7(A + 3) + 6$, $7(A + 9) + 1$, $7(A + 17) + 6$ or $7(A + 30) + 6$, so 7 does not divide a^3. Thus, since 7 divides a^3, 7 divides a, and $a = 7t$ for some integer t. Then, $a^3 = 343t^3 = 7b^3$, $b^3 = 49t^3$, so 7 divides b^3 and thus 7 divides b. This means that a and b both have 7 as a common factor. Contradiction.

EXERCISES 5.5, page 62

1. $(a, b)(c, d) = (ac - bd, ad + bc)$,

$(c, d)(a, b) = (ca - db, cb + da) = (ac - bd, ad + bc) = (a, b)(c, d)$

by the commutative property of addition and of multiplication for real numbers.

3. Since, if a and b are real numbers, $-a$ and $-b$ are real numbers, and $(-a, -b)$ is a complex number, then

$$(a, b) + (-a, -b) = (a + (-a), b + (-b)) = (0, 0).$$

5. If $(a, b) \ne (0, 0)$, $a \ne 0$ or $b \ne 0$, so $a^2 + b^2 \ne 0$, and thus $a/(a^2 + b^2)$ and $-b/(a^2 + b^2)$ are real numbers. In this case, $(a/(a^2 + b^2), -b/(a^2 + b^2))$ is a complex number, so letting $d = a^2 + b^2$, $(a, b)(a/(a^2 + b^2), -b/(a^2 + b^2)) = (a^2/d - (b)(-b)/d, ba/d + a(-b)/d) = ((a^2 + b^2)/d, (ab - ab)/d) = (d/d, 0) = (1, 0)$.

7. Pair the complex number $(a, 0)$ with the real number a. If $a + b = c$,

$$(a, 0) + (b, 0) = (a + b, 0) = (c, 0).$$

If $a \cdot b = c$, then

$$(a, 0)(b, 0) = (ab - 0, a \cdot 0 + b \cdot 0) = (ab, 0) = (c, 0).$$

INDEX